Dairy Diary 2021

Name
....

Address
....

....

Postcode
....

☎ Home
....

☎ Mobile
....

Email
....

....

In case of emergency contact:
....

Name
....

☎ Tel.
....

Website: dairydiary.co.uk
Blog: dairydiary.co.uk/blog
To order: 0344 4725265

PLANNER 2021

JANUARY		FEBRUARY		MARCH	
1	Fri BANK HOLIDAY UK	1	Mon	1	Mon
2	Sat	2	Tue	2	Tue
3	Sun	3	Wed	3	Wed
4	Mon BANK HOLIDAY SCOTLAND	4	Thu	4	Thu
5	Tue	5	Fri	5	Fri
6	Wed	6	Sat	6	Sat
7	Thu	7	Sun	7	Sun
8	Fri	8	Mon	8	Mon
9	Sat	9	Tue	9	Tue
10	Sun	10	Wed	10	Wed
11	Mon	11	Thu	11	Thu
12	Tue	12	Fri	12	Fri
13	Wed	13	Sat	13	Sat
14	Thu	14	Sun	14	Sun
15	Fri	15	Mon	15	Mon
16	Sat	16	Tue	16	Tue
17	Sun	17	Wed	17	Wed BANK HOLIDAY N. IRELAND
18	Mon	18	Thu	18	Thu
19	Tue	19	Fri	19	Fri
20	Wed	20	Sat	20	Sat
21	Thu	21	Sun	21	Sun
22	Fri	22	Mon	22	Mon
23	Sat	23	Tue	23	Tue
24	Sun	24	Wed	24	Wed
25	Mon	25	Thu	25	Thu
26	Tue	26	Fri	26	Fri
27	Wed	27	Sat	27	Sat
28	Thu	28	Sun	28	Sun
29	Fri			29	Mon
30	Sat			30	Tue
31	Sun			31	Wed

APRIL	MAY	JUNE
1 Thu	1 Sat	1 Tue
2 Fri BANK HOLIDAY UK	2 Sun	2 Wed
3 Sat	3 Mon BANK HOLIDAY UK	3 Thu
4 Sun	4 Tue	4 Fri
5 Mon BANK HOLIDAY UK (EXCL. SCOTLAND)	5 Wed	5 Sat
6 Tue	6 Thu	6 Sun
7 Wed	7 Fri	7 Mon
8 Thu	8 Sat	8 Tue
9 Fri	9 Sun	9 Wed
10 Sat	10 Mon	10 Thu
11 Sun	11 Tue	11 Fri
12 Mon	12 Wed	12 Sat
13 Tue	13 Thu	13 Sun
14 Wed	14 Fri	14 Mon
15 Thu	15 Sat	15 Tue
16 Fri	16 Sun	16 Wed
17 Sat	17 Mon	17 Thu
18 Sun	18 Tue	18 Fri
19 Mon	19 Wed	19 Sat
20 Tue	20 Thu	20 Sun
21 Wed	21 Fri	21 Mon
22 Thu	22 Sat	22 Tue
23 Fri	23 Sun	23 Wed
24 Sat	24 Mon	24 Thu
25 Sun	25 Tue	25 Fri
26 Mon	26 Wed	26 Sat
27 Tue	27 Thu	27 Sun
28 Wed	28 Fri	28 Mon
29 Thu	29 Sat	29 Tue
30 Fri	30 Sun	30 Wed
	31 Mon BANK HOLIDAY UK	P.T.O. July–December 2021

PLANNER 2021

JULY	AUGUST	SEPTEMBER
1 Thu	1 Sun	1 Wed
2 Fri	2 Mon BANK HOLIDAY SCOTLAND	2 Thu
3 Sat	3 Tue	3 Fri
4 Sun	4 Wed	4 Sat
5 Mon	5 Thu	5 Sun
6 Tue	6 Fri	6 Mon
7 Wed	7 Sat	7 Tue
8 Thu	8 Sun	8 Wed
9 Fri	9 Mon	9 Thu
10 Sat	10 Tue	10 Fri
11 Sun	11 Wed	11 Sat
12 Mon BANK HOLIDAY N. IRELAND	12 Thu	12 Sun
13 Tue	13 Fri	13 Mon
14 Wed	14 Sat	14 Tue
15 Thu	15 Sun	15 Wed
16 Fri	16 Mon	16 Thu
17 Sat	17 Tue	17 Fri
18 Sun	18 Wed	18 Sat
19 Mon	19 Thu	19 Sun
20 Tue	20 Fri	20 Mon
21 Wed	21 Sat	21 Tue
22 Thu	22 Sun	22 Wed
23 Fri	23 Mon	23 Thu
24 Sat	24 Tue	24 Fri
25 Sun	25 Wed	25 Sat
26 Mon	26 Thu	26 Sun
27 Tue	27 Fri	27 Mon
28 Wed	28 Sat	28 Tue
29 Thu	29 Sun	29 Wed
30 Fri	30 Mon BANK HOLIDAY UK (EXCL. SCOTLAND)	30 Thu
31 Sat	31 Tue	

OCTOBER	NOVEMBER	DECEMBER
1 Fri	1 Mon	1 Wed
2 Sat	2 Tue	2 Thu
3 Sun	3 Wed	3 Fri
4 Mon	4 Thu	4 Sat
5 Tue	5 Fri	5 Sun
6 Wed	6 Sat	6 Mon
7 Thu	7 Sun	7 Tue
8 Fri	8 Mon	8 Wed
9 Sat	9 Tue	9 Thu
10 Sun	10 Wed	10 Fri
11 Mon	11 Thu	11 Sat
12 Tue	12 Fri	12 Sun
13 Wed	13 Sat	13 Mon
14 Thu	14 Sun	14 Tue
15 Fri	15 Mon	15 Wed
16 Sat	16 Tue	16 Thu
17 Sun	17 Wed	17 Fri
18 Mon	18 Thu	18 Sat
19 Tue	19 Fri	19 Sun
20 Wed	20 Sat	20 Mon
21 Thu	21 Sun	21 Tue
22 Fri	22 Mon	22 Wed
23 Sat	23 Tue	23 Thu
24 Sun	24 Wed	24 Fri
25 Mon	25 Thu	25 Sat
26 Tue	26 Fri	26 Sun
27 Wed	27 Sat	27 Mon BANK HOLIDAY UK
28 Thu	28 Sun	28 Tue BANK HOLIDAY UK
29 Fri	29 Mon	29 Wed
30 Sat	30 Tue	30 Thu
31 Sun		31 Fri

Contents

The art of calm 26

Let's hear it for houseplants 28

Make your own natural dyes 30

USEFUL REMINDERS

PERSONAL

Bank

Beauty therapist

Building society

Citizen's Advice   citizensadvice.org.uk

  for England   03444 111 444

  for Wales   03444 77 20 20

Credit card emergency 1

Credit card emergency 2

Hairdresser

Life insurance policy number

  ☎ contact

  renewal date

Samaritans   116 123 (or local branch)

                        samaritans.org

Solicitor

Work

HEALTH

Blood group

Chemist

Chiropodist

Dentist

Doctor

Hospital

Medical insurance policy number

  ☎ contact

  renewal date

National insurance number

NHS (non-emergency)   111   nhs.uk

NHS number

Optician

Notes

8

HOME

Boiler service date

Childminder/nursery

Council

Electrician

Electricity provider

Gas engineer

Gas provider

Home insurance policy number

☎ contact

renewal date

Plumber

Police (non-emergency)   101   police.uk

School

TV licence renewal date

Vet

Water provider

TRAVEL

Car insurance policy number

☎ contact

renewal date

Breakdown service

Driving licence number

Garage

MOT due date

Road tax renewal date

Service date

Vehicle registration number

Eurostar   03432 186 186   eurostar.com

National Rail enq.   0345 748 4950

                     nationalrail.co.uk

Taxi

Passport adviceline   0300 222 0000

                     gov.uk/passport-advice-line

Passport number

renewal date

EHIC number

renewal date

Travel agent

Travel insurance policy number

☎ contact

renewal date

FAMILY & FRIENDS

Name

Address

☎ Home

   Work

   Mobile

Email

Name

Address

☎ Home

   Work

   Mobile

Email

Name

Address

☎ Home

   Work

   Mobile

Email

Name

Address

☎ Home

   Work

   Mobile

Email

Name

Address

☎ Home

   Work

   Mobile

Email

Name

Address

☎ Home

   Work

   Mobile

Email

Name

Address

☎ Home

Work

Mobile

Email

Name

Address

☎ Home

Work

Mobile

Email

Name

Address

☎ Home

Work

Mobile

Email

Name

Address

☎ Home

Work

Mobile

Email

Name

Address

☎ Home

Work

Mobile

Email

Name

Address

☎ Home

Work

Mobile

Email

FAMILY & FRIENDS

Name

Address

☎ Home

Work

Mobile

Email

Name

Address

☎ Home

Work

Mobile

Email

Name

Address

☎ Home

Work

Mobile

Email

Name

Address

☎ Home

Work

Mobile

Email

Name

Address

☎ Home

Work

Mobile

Email

Name

Address

☎ Home

Work

Mobile

Email

Name

Address

☎ Home

  Work

  Mobile

Email

Name

Address

☎ Home

  Work

  Mobile

Email

Name

Address

☎ Home

  Work

  Mobile

Email

Name

Address

☎ Home

  Work

  Mobile

Email

Name

Address

☎ Home

  Work

  Mobile

Email

Name

Address

☎ Home

  Work

  Mobile

Email

HOME BUDGETING

	JANUARY	FEBRUARY	MARCH
Opening balance			
Income			
New balance			
Birthdays/Christmas			
Car insurance			
Car MOT/service/tax			
Childcare			
Clothing/shoes			
Council tax			
Dentist/optician			
Electricity			
Entertainment			
Gas/oil/solid fuel			
Groceries			
Hairdresser			
Holidays			
Home/pet insurance			
Life/medical insurance			
Mobile/phone/internet			
Mortgage/rent			
Newspapers/magazines			
Petrol/fares			
Pets			
Savings			
TV licence/satellite			
Water			
Total expenditure			
Closing balance			

	APRIL	MAY	JUNE
Opening balance			
Income			
New balance			
Birthdays/Christmas			
Car insurance			
Car MOT/service/tax			
Childcare			
Clothing/shoes			
Council tax			
Dentist/optician			
Electricity			
Entertainment			
Gas/oil/solid fuel			
Groceries			
Hairdresser			
Holidays			
Home/pet insurance			
Life/medical insurance			
Mobile/phone/internet			
Mortgage/rent			
Newspapers/magazines			
Petrol/fares			
Pets			
Savings			
TV licence/satellite			
Water			
Total expenditure			
Closing balance			

HOME BUDGETING

	JULY	AUGUST	SEPTEMBER
Opening balance			
Income			
New balance			
Birthdays/Christmas			
Car insurance			
Car MOT/service/tax			
Childcare			
Clothing/shoes			
Council tax			
Dentist/optician			
Electricity			
Entertainment			
Gas/oil/solid fuel			
Groceries			
Hairdresser			
Holidays			
Home/pet insurance			
Life/medical insurance			
Mobile/phone/internet			
Mortgage/rent			
Newspapers/magazines			
Petrol/fares			
Pets			
Savings			
TV licence/satellite			
Water			
Total expenditure			
Closing balance			

	OCTOBER	NOVEMBER	DECEMBER
Opening balance			
Income			
New balance			
Birthdays/Christmas			
Car insurance			
Car MOT/service/tax			
Childcare			
Clothing/shoes			
Council tax			
Dentist/optician			
Electricity			
Entertainment			
Gas/oil/solid fuel			
Groceries			
Hairdresser			
Holidays			
Home/pet insurance			
Life/medical insurance			
Mobile/phone/internet			
Mortgage/rent			
Newspapers/magazines			
Petrol/fares			
Pets			
Savings			
TV licence/satellite			
Water			
Total expenditure			
Closing balance			

2020

January
Mon		6	13	20	27
Tue		7	14	21	28
Wed	1	8	15	22	29
Thu	2	9	16	23	30
Fri	3	10	17	24	31
Sat	4	11	18	25	
Sun	5	12	19	26	

February
Mon		3	10	17	24
Tue		4	11	18	25
Wed		5	12	19	26
Thu		6	13	20	27
Fri		7	14	21	28
Sat	1	8	15	22	29
Sun	2	9	16	23	

March
Mon		2	9	16	23	30
Tue		3	10	17	24	31
Wed		4	11	18	25	
Thu		5	12	19	26	
Fri		6	13	20	27	
Sat		7	14	21	28	
Sun	1	8	15	22	29	

April
Mon		6	13	20	27
Tue		7	14	21	28
Wed	1	8	15	22	29
Thu	2	9	16	23	30
Fri	3	10	17	24	
Sat	4	11	18	25	
Sun	5	12	19	26	

May
Mon		4	11	18	25
Tue		5	12	19	26
Wed		6	13	20	27
Thu		7	14	21	28
Fri	1	8	15	22	29
Sat	2	9	16	23	30
Sun	3	10	17	24	31

June
Mon	1	8	15	22	29
Tue	2	9	16	23	30
Wed	3	10	17	24	
Thu	4	11	18	25	
Fri	5	12	19	26	
Sat	6	13	20	27	
Sun	7	14	21	28	

July
Mon		6	13	20	27
Tue		7	14	21	28
Wed	1	8	15	22	29
Thu	2	9	16	23	30
Fri	3	10	17	24	31
Sat	4	11	18	25	
Sun	5	12	19	26	

August
Mon		3	10	17	24	31
Tue		4	11	18	25	
Wed		5	12	19	26	
Thu		6	13	20	27	
Fri		7	14	21	28	
Sat	1	8	15	22	29	
Sun	2	9	16	23	30	

September
Mon		7	14	21	28
Tue	1	8	15	22	29
Wed	2	9	16	23	30
Thu	3	10	17	24	
Fri	4	11	18	25	
Sat	5	12	19	26	
Sun	6	13	20	27	

October
Mon		5	12	19	26
Tue		6	13	20	27
Wed		7	14	21	28
Thu	1	8	15	22	29
Fri	2	9	16	23	30
Sat	3	10	17	24	31
Sun	4	11	18	25	

November
Mon		2	9	16	23	30
Tue		3	10	17	24	
Wed		4	11	18	25	
Thu		5	12	19	26	
Fri		6	13	20	27	
Sat		7	14	21	28	
Sun	1	8	15	22	29	

December
Mon		7	14	21	28
Tue	1	8	15	22	29
Wed	2	9	16	23	30
Thu	3	10	17	24	31
Fri	4	11	18	25	
Sat	5	12	19	26	
Sun	6	13	20	27	

2022

January
Mon		3	10	17	24	31
Tue		4	11	18	25	
Wed		5	12	19	26	
Thu		6	13	20	27	
Fri		7	14	21	28	
Sat	1	8	15	22	29	
Sun	2	9	16	23	30	

February
Mon		7	14	21	28
Tue	1	8	15	22	
Wed	2	9	16	23	
Thu	3	10	17	24	
Fri	4	11	18	25	
Sat	5	12	19	26	
Sun	6	13	20	27	

March
Mon		7	14	21	28
Tue	1	8	15	22	29
Wed	2	9	16	23	30
Thu	3	10	17	24	31
Fri	4	11	18	25	
Sat	5	12	19	26	
Sun	6	13	20	27	

April
Mon		4	11	18	25
Tue		5	12	19	26
Wed		6	13	20	27
Thu		7	14	21	28
Fri	1	8	15	22	29
Sat	2	9	16	23	30
Sun	3	10	17	24	

May
Mon		2	9	16	23	30
Tue		3	10	17	24	31
Wed		4	11	18	25	
Thu		5	12	19	26	
Fri		6	13	20	27	
Sat		7	14	21	28	
Sun	1	8	15	22	29	

June
Mon		6	13	20	27
Tue		7	14	21	28
Wed	1	8	15	22	29
Thu	2	9	16	23	30
Fri	3	10	17	24	
Sat	4	11	18	25	
Sun	5	12	19	26	

July
Mon		4	11	18	25
Tue		5	12	19	26
Wed		6	13	20	27
Thu		7	14	21	28
Fri	1	8	15	22	29
Sat	2	9	16	23	30
Sun	3	10	17	24	31

August
Mon	1	8	15	22	29
Tue	2	9	16	23	30
Wed	3	10	17	24	31
Thu	4	11	18	25	
Fri	5	12	19	26	
Sat	6	13	20	27	
Sun	7	14	21	28	

September
Mon		5	12	19	26
Tue		6	13	20	27
Wed		7	14	21	28
Thu	1	8	15	22	29
Fri	2	9	16	23	30
Sat	3	10	17	24	
Sun	4	11	18	25	

October
Mon		3	10	17	24	31
Tue		4	11	18	25	
Wed		5	12	19	26	
Thu		6	13	20	27	
Fri		7	14	21	28	
Sat	1	8	15	22	29	
Sun	2	9	16	23	30	

November
Mon		7	14	21	28
Tue	1	8	15	22	29
Wed	2	9	16	23	30
Thu	3	10	17	24	
Fri	4	11	18	25	
Sat	5	12	19	26	
Sun	6	13	20	27	

December
Mon		5	12	19	26
Tue		6	13	20	27
Wed		7	14	21	28
Thu	1	8	15	22	29
Fri	2	9	16	23	30
Sat	3	10	17	24	31
Sun	4	11	18	25	

2021

January

Mon		4	11	18	25
Tue		5	12	19	26
Wed		6	13	20	27
Thu		7	14	21	28
Fri	1	8	15	22	29
Sat	2	9	16	23	30
Sun	3	10	17	24	31

February

Mon	1	8	15	22	
Tue	2	9	16	23	
Wed	3	10	17	24	
Thu	4	11	18	25	
Fri	5	12	19	26	
Sat	6	13	20	27	
Sun	7	14	21	28	

March

Mon	1	8	15	22	29
Tue	2	9	16	23	30
Wed	3	10	17	24	31
Thu	4	11	18	25	
Fri	5	12	19	26	
Sat	6	13	20	27	
Sun	7	14	21	28	

April

Mon		5	12	19	26
Tue		6	13	20	27
Wed		7	14	21	28
Thu	1	8	15	22	29
Fri	2	9	16	23	30
Sat	3	10	17	24	
Sun	4	11	18	25	

May

Mon		3	10	17	24	31
Tue		4	11	18	25	
Wed		5	12	19	26	
Thu		6	13	20	27	
Fri		7	14	21	28	
Sat	1	8	15	22	29	
Sun	2	9	16	23	30	

June

Mon		7	14	21	28
Tue	1	8	15	22	29
Wed	2	9	16	23	30
Thu	3	10	17	24	
Fri	4	11	18	25	
Sat	5	12	19	26	
Sun	6	13	20	27	

July

Mon		5	12	19	26
Tue		6	13	20	27
Wed		7	14	21	28
Thu	1	8	15	22	29
Fri	2	9	16	23	30
Sat	3	10	17	24	31
Sun	4	11	18	25	

August

Mon		2	9	16	23	30
Tue		3	10	17	24	31
Wed		4	11	18	25	
Thu		5	12	19	26	
Fri		6	13	20	27	
Sat		7	14	21	28	
Sun	1	8	15	22	29	

September

Mon		6	13	20	27
Tue		7	14	21	28
Wed	1	8	15	22	29
Thu	2	9	16	23	30
Fri	3	10	17	24	
Sat	4	11	18	25	
Sun	5	12	19	26	

October

Mon		4	11	18	25
Tue		5	12	19	26
Wed		6	13	20	27
Thu		7	14	21	28
Fri	1	8	15	22	29
Sat	2	9	16	23	30
Sun	3	10	17	24	31

November

Mon	1	8	15	22	29
Tue	2	9	16	23	30
Wed	3	10	17	24	
Thu	4	11	18	25	
Fri	5	12	19	26	
Sat	6	13	20	27	
Sun	7	14	21	28	

December

Mon		6	13	20	27
Tue		7	14	21	28
Wed	1	8	15	22	29
Thu	2	9	16	23	30
Fri	3	10	17	24	31
Sat	4	11	18	25	
Sun	5	12	19	26	

Calendar dates

UK HOLIDAYS †	2021	2022
New Year	Jan 1	Jan 3
New Year (Scotland)	Jan 1/4*	Jan 3/4*
St Patrick's Day (Northern Ireland)	Mar 17	Mar 17
Good Friday	Apr 2	Apr 15
Easter Monday	Apr 5	Apr 18
Early Spring	May 3	May 2
Spring	May 31	May 30
Battle of the Boyne (Northern Ireland)	Jul 12	Jul 12
Summer (Scotland)	Aug 2	Aug 1
Summer (except Scotland)	Aug 30	Aug 29
Christmas Day	Dec 27*	Dec 27*
Boxing Day	Dec 28*	Dec 26

NOTABLE DATES	2021
Burns' Night	Jan 25
Holocaust Memorial Day	Jan 27
Accession of Queen Elizabeth II	Feb 6
Chinese New Year – Year of the Ox	Feb 12
St Valentine's Day	Feb 14
Shrove Tuesday (Pancake Day)	Feb 16
St David's Day (Wales)	Mar 1
Commonwealth Day	Mar 8
St Patrick's Day (Ireland)	Mar 17
Mothering Sunday	Mar 14
Birthday of Queen Elizabeth II	Apr 21
St George's Day (England)	Apr 23
World Red Cross/Red Crescent Day	May 8
Coronation Day	Jun 2
Queen's Official Birthday (t.b.c.)	Jun 12
Father's Day	Jun 20
Armed Forces' Day	Jun 26
St Swithin's Day	Jul 15
International Day of Peace	Sep 21
United Nations Day	Oct 24
Halloween	Oct 31
Armistice Day	Nov 11
Remembrance Sunday	Nov 14
Birthday of the Prince of Wales	Nov 14
St Andrew's Day (Scotland)	Nov 30

RELIGIOUS DATES

Christian

Epiphany	Jan 6
Ash Wednesday	Feb 17
Palm Sunday	Mar 28
Good Friday	Apr 2
Easter Day	Apr 4
Ascension Day	May 13
Whit Sunday, Pentecost	May 23
Trinity Sunday	May 30
Corpus Christi	Jun 3
Advent Sunday	Nov 28
Christmas Day	Dec 25

Buddhist

Parinirvana Day	Feb 15
Wesak (Buddha Day)	May 26
Bodhi Day (Buddha's enlightenment)	Dec 8

Hindu

Maha Shivaratri	Mar 11
Holi	Mar 29
Navaratri begins	Oct 6
Diwali begins (also celebrated by Sikhs)	Nov 4

Islamic

Ramadan begins	April 13
Eid Ul-Fitr	May 13
Eid Ul-Adha	Jul 20
Al-Hijra (New Year)	Aug 10
Milad un Nabi (Prophet's birthday)	Oct 19

Jewish

Purim begins	Feb 26
Pesach (Passover) begins	Mar 28
Shavuot (Pentecost) begins	May 17
Rosh Hashanah (Jewish New Year)	Sep 7
Yom Kippur (Day of Atonement)	Sep 16
Succoth (Tabernacles) begins	Sep 21
Chanukah begins	Nov 28

Sikh

These dates follow the Nanakshahi calendar

Birthday of Guru Gobind Singh	Jan 5
Vaisakhi	Apr 14
Birthday of Guru Nanak	Apr 14
Martyrdom of Guru Arjan Dev	Jun 16
Martyrdom of Guru Tegh Bahadur	Nov 24

Note: Many religious dates are based on the lunar calendar and, therefore, we cannot guarantee their accuracy.

PHASES OF THE MOON

● New moon			) First quarter		
	Day	H:M		Day	H:M
Jan	13	05:00	Jan	20	21:02
Feb	11	19:06	Feb	19	18:47
Mar	13	10:21	Mar	21	14:40
Apr	12	02:31	Apr	20	06:59
May	11	19:00	May	19	19:13
Jun	10	10:53	Jun	18	03:54
Jul	10	01:17	Jul	17	10:11
Aug	8	13:50	Aug	15	15:20
Sep	7	00:52	Sep	13	20:39
Oct	6	11:05	Oct	13	03:25
Nov	4	21:15	Nov	11	12:46
Dec	4	07:43	Dec	11	01:36

○ Full moon			(Last quarter		
	Day	H:M		Day	H:M
Jan	28	19:16	Jan	6	09:37
Feb	27	08:17	Feb	4	17:37
Mar	28	18:48	Mar	6	01:30
Apr	27	03:32	Apr	4	10:02
May	26	11:14	May	3	19:50
Jun	24	18:40	Jun	2	07:24
Jul	24	02:37	Jul	1	21:11
Aug	22	12:02	Jul	31	13:16
Sep	20	23:55	Aug	30	07:13
Oct	20	14:57	Sep	29	01:57
Nov	19	08.57	Oct	28	20:05
Dec	19	04:36	Nov	27	12:28
			Dec	27	02:24

BRITISH SUMMERTIME (t.b.c. by Government)

▶ Clocks go forward 1 hour at 1am on 28 March

◀ Clocks go back 1 hour at 2am on 31 October

SEASONS

	Month	Day	H:M
Vernal equinox Spring begins	Mar	20	09:37
Summer solstice Summer begins	June	21	03:32
Autumnal equinox Autumn begins	Sep	22	19:21
Winter solstice Winter begins	Dec	21	15:59

WEBSITES

gov.uk/bank-holidays

when-is.com

SUNRISE AND SUNSET TIMES

Note: times vary – these are for London

Day	Rise H:M	Set H:M	Day	Rise H:M	Set H:M	Day	Rise H:M	Set H:M	Day	Rise H:M	Set H:M
January			**February**			**March**			**April**		
07	08:05	16:10	07	07:29	17:01	07	06:32	17:52	07	06:22	19:44
14	08:00	16:20	14	07:16	17:14	14	06:17	18:04	14	06:07	19:56
21	07:53	16:31	21	07:02	17:27	21	06:01	18:16	21	05:52	20:08
28	07:45	16:43	28	06:48	17:39	28	06:45	19:28	28	05:38	20:19
May			**June**			**July**			**August**		
07	05:22	20:34	07	04:45	21:14	07	04:53	21:18	07	05:34	20:38
14	05:10	20:45	14	04:43	21:19	14	05:00	21:12	14	05:45	20:25
21	05:00	20:55	21	04:43	21:22	21	05:09	21:04	21	05:56	20:10
28	04:53	21:04	28	04:46	21:22	28	05:19	20:55	28	06:07	19:55
September			**October**			**November**			**December**		
07	06:23	19:33	07	07:11	18:25	07	07:05	16:23	07	07:52	15:52
14	06:34	19:17	14	07:23	18:09	14	07:17	16:12	14	07:59	15:52
21	06:45	19:01	21	07:35	17:55	21	07:29	16:04	21	08:04	15:54
28	06:57	18:45	28	07:47	17:41	28	07:40	15:57	28	08:06	15:58

Anniversaries

ROYAL ALBERT HALL
150 years

The Royal Albert Hall, Grade I listed, was opened on 29 March 1871. It was the vision of Prince Albert, who envisaged a permanent location to inspire and educate the public after the success of the 1851 Great Exhibition.

Queen Victoria's husband did not live to see his dream realised, dying of suspected typhoid fever in 1861. Construction paused until 1867 as a mark of respect. Though Victoria laid the foundation stone, she was too overcome with emotion to speak at the opening ceremony.

Today the hall fulfils Albert's vision as a leading destination for cultural events. It has hosted the *Proms* every summer since 1941 and an illustrious list of artists have graced its stage, including the Beatles, Nina Simone, the Rolling Stones and Led Zeppelin.

Its distinctive, glass cupola may have been its saving grace in WWII: disorientated Luftwaffe pilots allegedly used it to get their bearings over London. Its roof was painted black during the Blitz and though it was bombed on a few occasions, the hall and its 6 million red bricks remained largely intact.

2021 ANNIVERSARIES

450: The Royal Exchange is opened in London by Queen Elizabeth I (23 January 1571)

300: Robert Walpole becomes first Prime Minister of Great Britain (April 1721)

250: First recorded town cricket match at Horsham in Surrey (8 August 1771)

250: Birth of novelist Sir Walter Scott (15 August 1771)

200: Coronation of George IV as King of the United Kingdom of Great Britain and Ireland (19 July 1821)

175: Repeal of the Corn Laws (15 May 1846)

175: Opening of Albert Dock in Liverpool (30 July 1846)

150: Serialisation of George Eliot's novel *Middlemarch* begins (December 1871)

150: Death of Charles Babbage, considered the 'father of the computer' (18 October 1871)

120: Death of Queen Victoria (22 January 1901)

100: Province of Northern Ireland created within the United Kingdom under the terms of the Government of Ireland Act 1920 (3 May 1921)

75: First United Nations meeting held in London (10 January 1946)

75: Heathrow Airport opens for civilian use (31 May 1946)

75: TV licence is introduced, costing £2 (1 June 1946)

75: English premiere of J.B. Priestley's *An Inspector Calls* (1 October 1946)

50: Britain adopts the decimal currency with 20 shillings to a pound substituted by 100 new pence (15 February 1971)

50: The first Hard Rock Cafe opens on Old Park Lane in Mayfair, London (14 June 1971)

30: The World Wide Web is launched to the public (6 August 1991)

25: Birth of Dolly the Sheep, the first cloned mammal (5 July 1996)

25: The Spice Girls release their debut single *Wannabe* (July 1996)

25: The Prince and Princess of Wales, Charles and Diana, complete divorce proceedings after 15 years of marriage (28 August 1996)

15: Queen Elizabeth II celebrates her 80th birthday (21 April 2006)

FESTIVAL OF BRITAIN

70 years

In 1951 Britain was a nation in convalescence, slowly recovering from the ravages of the Second World War. Austerity measures had been in place for ten years and though it had been over half a decade since crowds danced in the streets on VE Day, rationing was still partially in place. The Festival of Britain was planned as a 'tonic for the nation', celebrating Britain's rich heritage and contributions to industry, science and culture. Its architects hoped it would rouse the spirits of a country in the grip of economic and social reform.

Though it was criticised by some for its perceived profligacy, events around the country helped to build a more optimistic view of Britain's standing in the world. It reshaped British design for a generation. The design of the garden cities of the 1950s was hugely influenced by the festival's aesthetic.

The main festival site was situated on London's South Bank and 8.5 million visited between May and September 1951. Of its futuristic structures, only the Royal Festival Hall remains. At the time, a 400-seater cinema called the Telekinema, the largest dome in the world (the Dome of

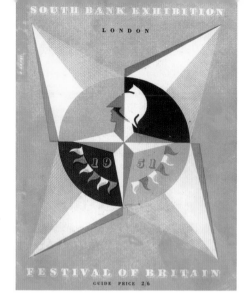

Discovery) and a visionary tower (the Skylon) also drew crowds. It is thought that around half of the population of Britain participated in the festival in some form. Linked exhibitions in Glasgow and Belfast documented the history of British engineering and farming respectively while many towns and villages held festival fêtes and events.

PEAK DISTRICT NATIONAL PARK

70 years

These days most Britons live just an hour from a national park. Yet there was a time when access to the countryside was by no means a given. From the 18th century onwards ownership of much of rural Britain had been transferred to private landowners even though industrial workers were eager to seek refuge from polluted cities in the countryside.

It would take many decades of campaigning until their 'right to roam' was enshrined in law. The Peak District National Park was finally created on 17 April 1951. The campaign included an organised mass trespass (known as the Kinder Scout trespass, after the Peak District's highest peak) by 500 ramblers. Some were jailed, only adding to calls for open access to the countryside.

Today the Peak District is one of 15 national parks in the UK. It spans five counties and 38,000 people live within its boundaries.

23

ANNIVERSARY & BIRTHDAY GIFT RECORD

WEDDINGS

1	Paper	14	Ivory
2	Cotton	15	Crystal
3	Leather	20	China
4	Books	25	Silver
5	Wood	30	Pearl
6	Iron	35	Coral
7	Wool	40	Ruby
8	Bronze	45	Sapphire
9	Copper	50	Gold
10	Tin	55	Emerald
11	Steel	60	Diamond
12	Silk	65	Blue
	or linen		Sapphire
13	Lace	70	Platinum

BIRTHSTONES AND FLOWERS

Month	Birthstone	Flower
January	Garnet	Carnation
February	Amethyst	Violet
March	Aquamarine	Jonquil
April	Diamond	Sweet Pea
May	Emerald	Lily of the Valley
June	Pearl	Rose
July	Ruby	Larkspur
August	Peridot	Gladiolus
September	Sapphire	Aster
October	Opal	Calendula
November	Topaz	Chrysanthemum
December	Turquoise	Narcissus

Name	Date	Ideas	Bought	Cost

ANNIVERSARY & BIRTHDAY GIFT RECORD

Name	Date	Ideas	Bought	Cost

The art of calm

In many ways, our lives are more taxing than ever before. Making an effort to incorporate moments of calm into your day can have positive effects for mind and body, including enhanced concentration and contentment. And you don't need long to reap the benefits.

There's no denying that modern life can be stressful. Faced with longer working hours and the magnetic tug of our smartphones, choosing calm in the midst of chaos can sometimes feel like an insurmountable task.

In today's technology-oriented society, it can be tricky to stay connected in the present. We are faced with a flood of information, whether in the form of news, television programmes, app notifications or messages from friends heralded by our buzzing smartphones. While being more connected than ever does have its benefits, it can also leave us aching for a quiet moment to ourselves.

It's not the being calm itself that is difficult, but remembering to slow down.

Should you find yourself stressed because you've taken on too much or your day has veered off course, taking a moment to gather your thoughts can be hugely beneficial for your state of mind. Opting to stay calm is a mindful act; a choice to be present and aware.

The best thing about adding mindful moments into your day is that over time, you will form a new habit. What's more, it doesn't have to mean retreating to a dark room to recite rounds of 'om'. It can be as simple as you like and adapted around your routine so that it becomes as much a part of the day as the school run or boiling the kettle.

JUST BREATHE

Paying attention to the breath is one of the simplest ways to introduce calm when your mind is racing. A round of deep breaths instantly slows the sympathetic nervous system, which controls the fight or flight response. Set an alarm on your phone or computer for a time when you know you might be feeling swamped, like returning after lunch to a full inbox. Choose a calming tone – a bell or singing birds – to sound the alarm, and to differentiate it from the beeps of notifications. When the alarm chimes, inhale deeply for at least four breaths to relieve tension. As you breathe in, become aware of the sensations in your body. Exhale for four beats. Repeat regularly.

LISTEN DEEPLY

Instead of focusing on your noisy thoughts, try concentrating on the sounds in your surroundings. Pay attention to whatever you can hear, noticing chirping birds or the white noise of the washing machine. Awakening this sense will lead you to notice the beauty in the present, in all its fullness.

SLOWLY DOES IT

If you're feeling overwhelmed, it can help to tackle each item on your to-do list in a conscious way by 'mono-tasking'. Say to yourself: "I'm going to do the washing-up for 10 minutes" or "I'll answer emails for 15 minutes". This can bring order to what might seem like a never-ending list.

GO WITH THE GREEN

Spending time in nature relaxes the mind and body. Research has proven that just being among trees lowers levels of the stress hormone cortisol in the body and can have beneficial effects on blood pressure and heart rate. You don't need to trek to your nearest forest to reap the benefits, either. Watering the plants or sipping your morning coffee outside can be just as soothing.

USE YOUR IMAGINATION

Visualisation may sound a little out there if you've never tried it, but it can be a fantastic way to reduce stress. It is the practice of imagining yourself in a safe, peaceful state, in a place that makes you feel relaxed. The human mind is astonishingly powerful, and by visualising tranquillity you will start to invoke calming feelings in the body, relieving tension. The power of visualisation has been backed by science as studies have found that the mere act of imagining creates new neural pathways. Set a 1-minute timer and imagine yourself in a place that makes you feel serene. Repeat throughout the day for best results.

SAVOUR SUPPERTIME

Ever find yourself wolfing down dinner without really focusing on what you're eating? Mealtimes, given how routinely they occur, offer a superb

opportunity to practise slowing down. Switch off autopilot and take your time noticing the texture, flavours and aromas of your meal. Eating more slowly will also do wonders for your digestion.

GIVE YOURSELF PERMISSION...

...to embrace imperfection. So much of the pressure we heap on ourselves is about reaching unattainable standards of perfection. You might be surprised to find there's joy in the not-quite-perfect. The Japanese have a word for this – wabi-sabi – which realises that the only constants in life are the three 'i's: impermanence, imperfection and incompleteness. Once we realise that nothing lasts and nothing can ever be perfect or 'finished', ourselves included, we free up our minds to focus on the present. And in so doing, adopting the art of calm suddenly feels much more achievable!

Let's hear it for houseplants!

If you were around in the 1970s, you might remember the decade's ubiquitous spider plants – perhaps you even nurtured one on your own windowsill. Today, houseplants are back in vogue and they can improve our wellbeing and enliven our homes.

Despite being very much on trend these days, the idea of bringing the outdoors in is nothing new: in this country houseplants have been on the scene since the late 1800s. Abroad, they have a longer history: indoor plants have long been seen as a marker of wealth and opulence in Asia. Chinese gardeners have been cultivating plants for decorative use in the home since 1000BC, so us Brits can hardly claim to be trendsetters!

In England houseplants were unheard of until they received a mention in Hugh Plat's gardening tome *The Garden of Eden* (1653). This inspired the wealthy to construct greenhouses, which were used to grow exotic plants for indoor use that would not have thrived outside in Britain.

GREEN GOODNESS

The surge in houseplants in UK homes in this century likely has less to do with their role as a status symbol and more to do with the fact that the average British adult spends 90% of their time inside*. Adding a plant to your space helps to bring the natural world indoors, so it makes sense that indoor plants provide many of the benefits of being outside in nature.

As well as livening up an empty corner or unloved windowsill, scientific studies have shown that houseplants improve physical health by purifying the air in our homes. The daily routine of tending to and watering plants can also reduce stress by acting as an exercise in mindfulness.

Visit any large supermarket or garden centre in Britain and you'll find row upon row of indoor greenery, from delicate ferns to towering Swiss cheese plants. The most reliable places to buy houseplants are reputable nurseries and garden centres, but even the droopiest of supermarket houseplants should perk up with a little TLC.

*Statistic by Opinium

SIX STARTER HOUSEPLANTS

If you are a houseplant beginner, try one of the six lush plants listed below. All can cope with a degree of neglect, making them a good starting point for those new to indoor greenery.

1 Jade plant (*Crassula ovata*) Jade plants prefer bright light, but are otherwise near impossible to kill. They are often called money plants as their rounded leaves resemble coins.

2 Mother-in-law's tongue (*Sansevieria*) This ironically-named decorative plant is often awarded the title of 'most indestructible houseplant'. It will adapt to most conditions.

3 Spider plant (*Chlorophytum comosum*) Arachnophobes, don't let the name put you off: this trailing plant is incredibly easy to care for and produces an endless stream of spider plant babies. You'll soon be pawning them off on unsuspecting friends and family!

4 Kalanchoe (*K. blossfeldiana*) Native to arid regions, this adaptable succulent blooms over a long period and comes in red, orange, pink, yellow and white flowering varieties.

5 Peace lily (*Spathiphyllum*) White, trumpet-shaped flowers make this a show-stopping choice. It is perfect for indoor flora novices because its leaves will droop noticeably when it needs watering.

6 Cast iron plant (*Aspidistra*) For a genuinely indestructible houseplant, opt for a cast iron plant, so nicknamed by the Victorians for its strength in the face of extreme neglect. Its glossy leaves will tolerate cold, heat, all manner of pests – and weeks without watering!

TIPS FOR BEGINNERS

The most likely reason for a houseplant's failure to thrive is overwatering. Most of the species of houseplants common in the UK are native to tropical regions where they are used to searing heat and high humidity, with an occasional drenching by way of tropical storms. As such, daily watering can leave them sulking. It's always advisable to check the needs of specific plants on the internet or the label, but as a general rule most houseplants do better with a thorough watering once a week.

Half of the battle of keeping houseplants alive is understanding their individual needs. Take your time to learn about growing conditions, paying particular attention to the amount of light preferred by the plants you have chosen. There's little point trying to force a sun-loving plant into an existence spent in a gloomy corner. To avoid becoming overwhelmed, it makes sense to build a houseplant collection slowly, getting to know your plants one by one.

It is also wise to avoid extremes of temperature. Many houseplants, including the popular Swiss cheese plant (*Monstera deliciosa*), prefer gentle sunlight. Direct sun can scorch the leaves. Central heating can also wreak havoc on the delicate ecosystem most indoor plants prefer so avoid placing pots too close to radiators.

As with most pastimes, raising happy houseplants tends to be a matter of trial and error. You will learn as you go, and come to accept that you might experience a few failures along the way. In the process, you'll jazz up your surroundings with some living decoration, boost the air quality inside your home and likely bring a smile to your face as well.

Make your own natural dyes

Natural dyeing is back in fashion thanks to growing environmental concerns. Making your own colours at home with things you already have in the kitchen cupboard is rewarding and rather addictive, and in doing so you'll be taking part in a long and ancient tradition.

What exactly is natural dyeing, you might ask? It's a valid question given that many people's experience with DIY dyeing is limited to childhood tie-dye experiments in a bucket or the rainbow rows of machine-washable Dylon packets found at the supermarket.

As the name suggests, natural dyeing involves making coloured dyes from ingredients present in nature. Although a growing aversion to chemical products has put natural dyeing in the spotlight, the practice is actually an ancient one. Before the invention of synthetic dyes in 1856, humans had been resourcefully brewing their own colours

for hundreds of years. These dyes were used to impart colour to household textiles and clothing.

Throughout history there are numerous examples of people dyeing fabrics using local foodstuffs, plants and spices, producing an array of dazzling colours. In Asia, saffron was used to produce yellow. Closer to home, red was created from a dye extracted from the common madder plant. Lichen was used for purple and at the height of the English wool trade, woad was used for a brilliant blue.

In industrial settings synthetic dyes are still used almost exclusively, but natural dyes continue to enjoy a quiet popularity among artists. As concern about industrial pollution grows, natural dyes are gaining appeal as a renewable resource with a low environmental footprint.

GETTING STARTED

Trying natural dyeing at home is easy and fun, and a great craft project to try with children during the school holidays. First, gather the materials you'll use to make your colours. Refer to the list of common household ingredients and the colours they produce (see right) for inspiration. Some substances provide an unexpected surprise – who would have guessed avocado stones would produce such a gentle shade of rose?

MATERIALS AND TOOLS

When selecting items to dye, choose your fabrics carefully. Synthetic fabrics, such as nylon and polyester, cannot be dyed using natural dyeing methods. Stick to cotton, wool, silk or older linen (which will take the dye better than new).

Some plant dyes need a 'mordant' to make their colour last, while others (such as avocado stones and tea) contain natural tannins that help bond the colour to the fabric. The most widely available mordant is soya milk. Soak your fabric

A RAINBOW OF COLOURS

Dye substance	Colour produced
Avocado skins/stones	Pale pink
Black beans	Blue
Blackcurrants	Purple
Brown onion skins	Orange
Coffee grounds	Brown
Daffodil heads	Yellow
Walnuts	Pale pink
Hibiscus flowers	Red
Red onion skins	Yellow
Rooibos tea	Peachy orange
Stinging nettles	Green
Turmeric	Yellow

in the diluted milk a few days before you wish to dye it, then wash in the machine, air-dry and repeat the process twice more for best results. Plant dyes which require pre-mordanted fabric include onion skins and turmeric.

Experiment with different foods and plants to see which colours you can create. Once you start, you'll begin to see potential dyeing projects all around you – in kitchen scraps, unloved weeds, flowers, the tea cupboard… When it comes to natural dyes, the joy is in the experimentation.

DIY PLANT-DYED TEA TOWEL

Makes enough dye to colour 3-5 tea towels

You will need:
Rubber gloves
Large, deep saucepan or pot
Water
4-6 avocado stones
Heatproof tongs or ladle
100% cotton or linen tea towels

1 Put on the rubber gloves. Fill the pan or pot with water until two-thirds full.
2 Add the avocado stones. Bring the water to a rolling boil, then reduce to a simmer.
3 Simmer the water for 30-60 minutes until it turns bright red.
4 Remove the stones with tongs or a ladle, then add the tea towels, keeping the liquid gently simmering.
5 After 15-20 minutes, the tea towels should be a light, peachy shade of pink. Soak for a longer period to achieve a deeper shade of pink.

6 When the tea towels reach the desired colour, use tongs to remove them from the pot. Rinse in warm water, then hang to dry out of direct sunlight.
7 To preserve the colour of your tea towel, wash on a cold wash after use and do not dry in direct sunlight.
TIP Repurpose old textiles to make your tea towels. Try tired, white duvet covers or pillowcases.

Quirky museums

From old operating theatres to sewing machine shrines, Britain is full of hidden treasures if you know where to find them. Diverge from the beaten path and you'll find yourself captivated, enthralled - and perhaps a little off colour - at these curiously kooky establishments around the UK.

SEWING MACHINE MUSEUM, LONDON

This museum in Tooting Bec is hidden away on the upper floor of an industrial warehouse and opens for just three hours every month. Its broad collection of sewing machines makes it worth the trip for keen or would-be seamstresses and will have you itching to get out your needle and thread at home.

A focal point is the sewing machine created for Queen Victoria's daughter in honour of her wedding in 1858. Kensington Palace is etched into the machine's scratch blade.

The exhibits are part of the personal collection of sewing machine salesman Ray Rushton, whose business is located in the same building. This means you even have the opportunity to purchase a selection of haberdashery items as you exit through the gift shop!

Exhibits ranging from Roman shoes to shrunken heads and a mummified crocodile.

THE PITT RIVERS MUSEUM, OXFORD

Set up in 1844 with a founding gift of 26,000 objects from the personal collection of General Pitt Rivers, this treasure trove of oddities now contains an astonishing half a million objects. Glass cabinet after glass cabinet brims with curious exhibits ranging from Roman shoes to shrunken heads and even a mummified crocodile.

THE NATIONAL PIPING CENTRE, GLASGOW

The Museum of Piping located at the National Piping Centre charts three hundred years of piping heritage, including bagpipes from Argyll dating back to the 1700s. European bagpipes are also on show, with Polish, Spanish, Hungarian and Italian examples exhibited. Visitors have an opportunity to try out a set of bagpipes for themselves – ear plugs optional!

THE OLD OPERATING THEATRE MUSEUM & HERB GARRET, LONDON

Situated in the attic of the early-18th century chapel of St Thomas' Hospital in Southwark, this atmospheric museum offers fascinating insight into the history of medicine and the early days of surgery. The faint of heart may wish to skip the herb garret, which includes a small operating theatre. This was used between 1821 and 1862 – the era before the invention of general anaesthetic. Weekly talks detail the intricacies and gore of medicine in centuries past and sometimes include Victorian surgery demonstrations.

DERWENT PENCIL MUSEUM, KESWICK

This special interest collection in Cumbria can surely claim one of the quirkiest entrances to a museum in the country: visitors enter through a replica of the mine where graphite, used to make pencil lead, was first discovered in the 1550s. From there, follow the history of pencil manufacturing from the Elizabethan era to the present day. View the Queen's Diamond Jubilee pencil and the largest pencil in the world, among many other historic writing instruments. There is also a quiz designed especially for children, making this museum apt for a family adventure.

TEAPOT ISLAND, MAIDSTONE

This family-run, Kentish museum seems appropriately located in a country known for its fondness for a cup of Rosie Lee. The owners, a mother and son, pride themselves on the fact that there are no duplicates among their collection of almost 7,000 teapots, which manifests a clear penchant for novelty teapots. Once you've exhausted the viewing collection, you can recharge with a mug of tea (of course!) in the museum's neighbouring tea room.

BACK TO BACKS, BIRMINGHAM

The National Trust has preserved the last surviving court of so-called back-to-back houses, which provided homes around a single, shared courtyard for the 19th century working classes. Accessible by pre-booked guided tour only, a visit charts the working lives of former residents who lived and worked there in close quarters between the 1840s and the 1970s. Pick up a paper bag of pear drops from 'Candies', a working sweetshop still peddling sugary tuck from its beautifully preserved 1930s interior. Visitors can also snoop around the kitchen of a long-ago resident, which has been restored to its former condition.

HOUSE OF MARBLES, BOVEY TRACEY

For a fun-filled family day out on the edge of Dartmoor National Park, look no further than the wonderfully bizarre House of Marbles. This interactive museum on the site of a working glassworks is sure to keep children entertained for hours with its assortment of marble runs, fairground mirrors and a giant floating marble. Adult visitors might also enjoy the site's listed kilns, as this is an historic location of pottery making.

THE FAN MUSEUM, LONDON

Feeling flushed? You'll enjoy a trip to The Fan Museum, located in Greenwich, and home to over 5,000 fans from around the world. The museum's oldest artefacts date back to the 12th century and the collection includes a number of commemorative fans.

Where the wild things are

Britain has historically been home to a wealth of flora and fauna for a nation of its size. But over the past century, intensive farming and invasive disease have seen much of Britain's wildlife vanish at a startling rate.

You might not associate the term 'wild' with the genteel image of the British countryside that sits firmly in the popular imagination. Yet the British Isles are home to an abundance of stunning habitats from a long coastline to sprawling farmlands; freshwater ecosystems to expansive moorlands. In turn, these habitats provide homes for a diverse array of wildlife.

City gardens and built-up towns also provide valuable havens for some of Britain's best-loved animals. Wildlife can be found even in the most urban environments, whether in the form of a city centre park or a window box on a polluted street. In fact, green space in cities is arguably even more vital, providing havens for birds, bees and more.

Unfortunately, Britain's wildlife is struggling and this has been the case for some time. Although almost a third of the UK's land lies within protected areas, much of the countryside has been altered by agriculture, urbanisation and forest clearing over the past century.

Reports show that over half of British species have declined since 1970. Habitat loss due to intensive farming, pesticide use and diseases brought from abroad have all been contributing factors. Bats, butterflies, hedgehogs, sparrows, skylarks and stag beetles are just a few of the many species that have been negatively affected by these changes. Today, one in ten of the UK's wildlife species faces extinction.

GOOD NEWS

There are, however, glimmers of hope on the horizon, which serve as a welcome reminder that a few small steps really can make a significant difference.

Urban bird populations are maintaining a steady presence: goldfinches and long-tailed tits, in particular, have seen increases in their numbers. Latest figures suggest more than half of British homeowners regularly put out food for garden birds throughout the year, which is part of the reason why populations of garden birds are holding firm. The resurgence of red kites in much of England and Scotland is testament to the fact that, when properly and sensibly implemented, conservation methods can work wonders.

Meanwhile, two-thirds of British butterfly species are showing an uptick in numbers. Otters are now found in every county in England. A set of stamps released by Royal Mail in 2018 commemorated the successful reintroduction of previously extinct animals, including the osprey, Eurasian beaver, pool frog and large blue butterfly.

EXODUS OF THE BIRDS

Roughly 230 species of birds call the British Isles home, and a further 230 migratory species pass some of the year enjoying the UK's mild climate. Unfortunately, however, a quarter of UK birds, including curlews, puffins and nightingales, are unlikely to survive without immediate conservation measures. Nearly two-thirds of Britain's skylarks and lapwings have vanished, as reported in the European bird census.

CREEPY-CRAWLY CRISIS

Insects and other invertebrates have been particularly badly affected. In pollinating vital crops and ensuring soil is healthy and fertile, they perform one of the most crucial roles in our ecosystem. Without them, the future of the food system we rely on would look very dire indeed. Bees are the focus of many rewilding efforts in the UK, given the news that wild bees and hoverflies have been badly affected by insecticide use. Ants and beetles, meanwhile, are disappearing eight times faster than mammals and birds in the same regions, according to analysis by *Biological Conservation*.

VANISHING FLORA

It's not just Britain's fauna that are facing a catalogue of severe threats. Flora, too, is bearing the brunt of intensive agriculture, extreme weather and increased use of pesticides. Where fifty years ago, vast wildflower meadows – featuring the swaying blooms and seed heads of wild orchids, poppies, cowslips and more – were a common sight dotting the British countryside, today one in five British wildflower species is threatened with extinction.

Gardening for wildlife

There's no doubt that we are a nation of gardeners, with 24 million gardens up and down the country. With many creatures in decline, there's no time like the present to turn your green space into a mini nature reserve. With a little effort, your garden could become a sanctuary for local wildlife.

How we tend to our gardens can have wide-reaching effects on the wildlife that is able to survive and thrive in them. When combined, Britain's residential gardens cover an area larger than all of the country's National Nature Reserves put together! What's more, a quarter of our cities and towns are made up of garden space.

While your own patch might seem too small to make a difference, by working as communities to foster wildlife in our green spaces, the nation's gardeners can link city plots with the countryside. A few straightforward changes to the way you garden make a world of difference. In the process, you'll make your outdoor space a lovely place to spend time, humming with life, colour and movement.

Stay away from using artificial pesticides.

THE BASICS

Wildlife requires just four essentials to thrive – food, water, shelter and somewhere to breed. By providing these elements, you will be well on your way to fostering a haven for flora and fauna and bringing your garden to life.

Encouraging wildlife in your garden can be as simple or as involved as you'd like. In fact, you might be glad to hear that embracing your inner lazy gardener will go a long way. Easing off the deadheading of spent flowers leaves a wonderful, energy-rich source of food for birds and small mammals. Similarly, while many rightly love the emerald neatness of a freshly cut lawn, stepping away from the lawnmower can bring many benefits for nature. Mowing just once a month instead of once a week can give invertebrates, butterflies and wildflowers the chance to thrive.

If you can go all summer without cutting the grass, you will find your lawn transformed into a thriving wild meadow providing shelter for all kinds of life. If you can't quite bring yourself to go that far, try leaving a strip of lawn at the end of your garden to grow long as a compromise. Allowing even a small patch to go to seed will create a sheltered oasis for beetles and other insects, while small birds will have the chance to feast on the seed heads come autumn.

GARDEN VARIETY

Variety is the spice of life, so the saying goes, and this is particularly true in a wildlife-friendly garden! The more habitats you create and the greater the diversity of the plants you grow, the more fauna you are likely to attract.

ENCOURAGE BUTTERFLIES

Butterfly-friendly planting is so simple that you might find your garden is already doing quite a bit to help these beautiful, winged visitors.

Draw butterflies in with flowers rich in nectar: scabious, honeysuckle and verbena are all good options. Make sure the plants in your garden or green space do not all flower at once - it's important to make sure butterflies have something to feed on in spring, summer and autumn. Try primroses in spring; lavender, red

valerian and buddleia in summer, and opt for Michaelmas daisies and ice-plants that will flower into autumn when butterflies might otherwise be going hungry.

BOOST FOR THE BEES

Bees are essential to our food chain, so essential that every third forkful of food consumed in Britain would not be possible without these furry, black and yellow creatures. Bees are even reported to contribute £650m to our economy! As with butterflies, planting a wide array of nectar-rich flowers and shrubs is a massive boon for these hungry pollinators.

The busiest feeding period for bees runs from early spring to late autumn, but planting some winter-flowering plants and shrubs is a way to provide sustenance in milder areas where these pollinators remain active all year.

Relax on the weeding, too – many flowering weeds, including dandelions, are a vital source of food for bees early in the year. Fruit trees, particularly apple trees and the crab apple, also provide excellent nourishment.

If you see a struggling bumblebee on the pavement, looking as if it's unable to lift its wings, it is likely not dead or dying but in need of some sustenance. You can help it on its way by mixing a little sugar with some water on a teaspoon and placing it beside the exhausted chap. All being well, the bee should enjoy its fill, perk up quickly and recover to pollinate many of the lovely, bee-friendly plants you've added to your garden!

HELP THE HEDGEHOGS

Though hedgehog numbers have fallen by 30% since 1970*, they are still found all over the UK, with the exception of just a few of the Scottish islands. These prickly pals love to roam, regularly travelling up to 2 miles a night – quite the feat for such a small creature! To help them on their way, leave a little hole at the bottom of your fence that hedgehogs can crawl through. If that's not possible, you can achieve the same effect by digging a narrow channel beneath the fence or garden boundary. The Wildlife Trusts suggests enlisting your neighbours to create a hedgehog highway between gardens.

You can also create nesting and hibernation sites for hedgehogs by leaving log or leaf piles around your garden and letting compost heaps go unturned over winter. Just take care to check for sleeping hedgehogs before lighting a bonfire or mowing long grass. If you're concerned about the hedgehogs in your area going hungry in the leaner months, put out a dish of wet dog or cat food and a bowl of fresh water.

SAVE THE BIRDS

The sight of birds frolicking in your garden is sure to give you a happy boost. To keep feathered friends well-nourished, put out nuts, seeds, suet cakes or fat balls in feeders, trays and on the ground. Stay away from using artificial pesticides: birds love to eat slugs and will quickly find their prey if you give them a chance to. A large bowl or shallow pot filled with tap water can act as an instant DIY bird bath; add a few stones or some gravel to the bottom to give birds a firmer footing.

*Statistic by The UK Mammal Society and Natural England

10 TIPS FOR PLANNING A WILDLIFE-FRIENDLY GARDEN

1 Opt for native trees and shrubs. These provide berries and seeds for birds and small mammals to eat. Examples include hawthorn, dog-rose, elder, ash, beech and field maples, but the list is long, so it's worth doing your own research. You might find you already have one or two in your garden!

2 Creating a pond in your garden is one of the best things you can do to benefit wildlife, attracting newts, toads, bathing birds and pond skaters. There's no need to invest in expensive landscaping either. Making a pond can be as simple as filling an empty pot with rainwater or repurposing an old bucket or tin bath. Just remember to check that there are no drainage holes in the bottom.

3 Swap your fence for a native hedge. Beech, hazel or hawthorn are good options. A hedge provides pollen, nectar, berries and seeds for birds and insects, and also allows roaming hedgehogs easy access to your garden.

4 While using pesticides can be tempting when faced with an invasion of aphids or leaf-munching slugs, avoiding artificial solutions will encourage natural predators such as frogs, birds, bats and ladybirds.

5 Although some consider it a nuisance, ivy provides vital nourishment for birds and bees throughout the year. Avoid cutting back after flowering to allow wildlife to reap the benefits.

6 Plant a herb garden. Flowering herbs such as rosemary and marjoram are a wonderful source of nectar. Bees also love borage, a medicinal herb with edible leaves and star-shaped flowers that makes a stunning addition to any self-respecting kitchen garden.

7 Choose single-flowering plants. Bees and other pollinating insects can find it difficult to climb into flowers with double petals and single flowers provide more sustenance than their dual-flowered relatives.

8 Did you know that your choice of compost could affect the wildlife in the wider countryside? Choose peat-free compost when buying soil for your garden or allotment: the harvesting of peat damages peat bog habitats, which are home to some of the rarest insects in Britain.

9 Start a compost heap in an unloved corner and a whole host of life will quickly move in. It will provide a habitat and sources of food for worms, fungi, toads, newts and even hedgehogs. Aim for a good balance of greens (grass clippings, plants) and browns (newspapers, woody cuttings, fallen leaves) in your compost.

10 Sow flowers in their multitudes, choosing heritage varieties where available. You will attract dozens of bees and butterflies, and you won't be able to stop yourself smiling when faced with such a colourful, blooming garden.

NO SPACE IS TOO SMALL

While gardening in small spaces might require a little extra creativity, a pint-sized patch is by no means an obstacle to helping the wildlife in your surroundings. Even a solitary window box can provide pollen for passing bees and butterflies.

• Oregano, thyme and marjoram do well in containers and are loved by pollinators. And you'll have a supply of fresh herbs for much of the year!

• It is possible to create a miniature wildlife pond in even the tiniest of gardens by repurposing an old bucket or disused sink.

• Think skywards by growing vertically. Climbing plants like honeysuckle, star jasmine and clematis are adored by bees and provide valuable nesting materials for birds.

Cooking with flowers

Cooking with edible flowers might seem like a modern trend, but floral dishes in fact draw on an ancient tradition that can be traced back to the Romans. Edible blooms contribute a genuine wow factor to a meal, adding texture, flavour and colour to both sweet and savoury dishes.

The ancient Greeks are believed to have added violets to their wine, while the imperial Chinese preferred their tipples brewed with chrysanthemums. Meanwhile, the Ottoman penchant for Turkish delight is yet another instance of flowers in gastronomic history. While the recent resurgence of cooking with flowers might be attributed to their good looks, making them perfect for the Instagram era, the roots of cooking with flowers run centuries deep.

In Britain, interest in edible blooms peaked in Victorian times: the era saw a new enthusiasm for flowers in all areas, including floriography, otherwise known as 'the language of flowers'. The heightened significance of

A few scattered petals can elevate the appearance of a dish.

flowers and their associated symbolism had our 19th century forebears adding violets, primroses and borage blossoms to their meals. Petals were added to salads, used to decorate cakes or even pickled in vinegar.

Nowadays, as the appeal of local food continues to grow, native flowers frequently feature on the menus of Michelin-starred restaurants and farm shop cafés alike. A few scattered petals can elevate the appearance of a dish, adding an elegant and aesthetically pleasing touch. And should you choose to add flowers to your food, you are taking part in a time-worn tradition, motivated by the simple desire to make meals even more appetising and attractive.

SOURCING EDIBLE FLOWERS

When it comes to sourcing flowers to eat, there are three main options: grow, buy or forage! Some supermarkets now stock edible flower punnets specifically for use in cooking, but you'll mostly be buying cut flowers to put in the pan. For this reason, it's important to opt for untreated flowers that haven't been sprayed with preservatives. If growing your own, care for plants accordingly and avoid weedkillers.

Foraging for edible flowers is another option. The bright hues make wild flowers easier to spot than greenery, so it's an activity for curious children too. If you live in a city, foraging for edible flowers is still possible, but steer clear of busy roads or industrial areas where flowers might have been contaminated by pollutants.

The availability of edible flowers in the wild is seasonal, but there is almost always something to find apart from in deep winter. In spring, the cream heads of elderflower can be used to make cordial or decorate bakes. Elder leaves and bark are poisonous, so use the blossoms only. In summer, instead of cursing the dandelions poking up in your lawn, why not scatter the heads over salads? Once you tune into the possibilities, you'll see edible flowers everywhere.

HINTS AND TIPS

- Wash flowers before use, or you might find a crunchy surprise in the form of an insect!
- Add edible flowers to salads for colour, texture and flavour. Nasturtium leaves are a great choice to add a spicy kick.
- Arrange small, whole flowers (try violets, violas or pansies) in ice cube trays, top up with water and freeze for stunning floral ice cubes.
- Add a few untreated rose petals to jam and preserve recipes for a floral twist.
- Most large supermarkets stock rosewater, orange blossom extract and botanical gins. You can add these to icings or glazes for floral bakes that are subtle but not overpowering.
- Many bolting edible plants produce blooms as they go to seed. If you grow your own broccoli or kale, add their yellow blossoms to stir-fries. Courgette flowers are an Italian delicacy. Most

USING EDIBLE FLOWERS

Remember not all blooms are edible: some are endangered while others can cause serious harm if consumed. Do your research and if in doubt, err on the side of caution. If buying edible flowers, always purchase from a florist or supermarket.

recipes recommend stuffing with soft cheese and herbs before deep-frying in batter.
- The flowers of most common herbs are safe to eat. Chive, rosemary and coriander flowers are all delicious ways to add flowers to dishes.
- Edible flowers can also be used as natural food colourings. Calendula (yellow) was historically put to use to colour butter and rice while dried rose petals add colour to icings.
- If you suffer from hayfever or other plant-related allergies, it is a good idea to remove the stamen and pistils of flowers before eating.

SIX COMMON EDIBLE FLOWERS

1 **Calendula** Also known as pot marigolds, these yellow and orange flowers have a flavour often likened to saffron.

2 **Cornflower** The purple petals of this hardy annual flower have a spicy, clove-like taste.

3 **Lavender** The delicate, lilac sprigs add sweetness to baked goods and a little goes a long way. Whole sprigs can also be used to garnish roast meats.

4 **Nasturtium** Easy to grow (though they prefer poorer soils), nasturtiums have a peppery kick not unlike watercress. In addition to its edible flowers and leaves, the seeds can be pickled for an unusual alternative to capers.

4 **Rose** The petals of the English national flower are faintly perfumed and can be used for decorative purposes or to make homemade rosewater for culinary use. Darker-coloured roses tend to have a stronger flavour. Remember to use untreated roses.

6 **Sweet violet, viola and pansy** These small flowers are subtly aromatic and their diminutive size means they are perfect for using as a garnish or for cake decoration.

DO-IT-YOURSELF CANDIED FLOWERS

Try this simple recipe for crystallised blooms. It provides reliably satisfying results, making it a great project to try with older children.

1 Gather a selection of small edible flowers: calendula, violets and pansies are classic choices, but you should feel free to use whichever edible petals you have on hand.

2 Gently beat an egg white with a teaspoon of water. Lightly coat the petals using a small brush, then sprinkle over caster sugar. Leave overnight to dry on a sheet of baking paper on a baking tray, then store in an airtight container.

3 They will keep for a few days and can be used to decorate cakes, biscuits or other baked goods.

SPICED ELDERFLOWER CORDIAL

Caster sugar 1kg (2lb 4oz)
Boiling water 900ml (1½ pints)
Citric acid 50g (2oz)
Elderflower heads 20, flowers snipped from stems
Lemon 1, thinly sliced
Limes 4, thinly sliced
Root ginger 50-75g (2-3oz), peeled & sliced

1 Put sugar in a bowl, add boiling water and stir until dissolved. Add citric acid and elderflowers; stir. Stir in sliced lemon, limes and ginger. Cover with clingfilm and put in a cool place for 6 days, stirring daily.
2 Place a colander or sieve over a bowl and line with muslin or clean J-cloths. Pour boiling water through to sterilise. Pour away water and wring out cloth.
3 Re-line sieve or colander, replace over bowl and strain the cordial through it. Discard elderflowers, lemon, limes and ginger.
4 Pour cordial through a funnel into two sterilised 75cl (1¼ pint) wine bottles. Seal with corks or screw caps and store in fridge. Will keep for a year or more. Serve diluted with chilled white wine, tonic or soda water, or top up with boiling water to make a hot toddy.

Makes 1½ litres (2½ pints) • Time 6 days
Calories 284 • Fibre 0.1g • Salt 0g • Sugar 75g
Fat 0g of which 0g is saturated

ICED LAVENDER LOAF

Milk 75ml (2½fl oz)
Fresh lavender flower heads 6, plus extra for decoration, or 1 tsp dried lavender
Unsalted butter 175g (6oz) softened
Caster sugar 175g (6oz)
Lemon 1, finely grated zest
Eggs 3, beaten
Self-raising flour 175g (6oz)
Icing sugar 225g (8oz)
Violet food colouring

1 Put milk and flower heads, or dried lavender, in a small pan and bring slowly to simmering over a low heat. Remove from heat, cover and set aside for 30 minutes. Strain milk into a bowl and discard lavender.
2 Preheat oven to 180°C/160°fan/Gas 4. Beat butter, caster sugar and zest until creamy. Gradually beat in eggs, adding a tablespoon of flour with each egg. Fold in remaining flour and 2 tablespoons of lavender milk.
3 Spoon mixture in two loaf tins; level the tops. Stand tins on a baking sheet and bake for 35 minutes or until a skewer comes out clean. Cool in tins for 10 minutes before turning out onto a wire rack to cool completely.
4 Sieve icing sugar into a bowl. Stir in enough lavender milk to make a smooth paste that just holds its shape. Tint icing by mixing in a little food colouring, then

Makes 2 loaves • Time 35 mins per loaf
Calories 235 • Fibre 0.4g • Salt 0.2g • Sugar 26.3g
Fat 10.2g of which 6.1g is saturated

spread it over the tops of the cakes with a palette knife. Decorate each cake with small sprigs of lavender flowers. Leave to set before serving.

Cook's information

DRY WEIGHT CONVERSIONS

grams (g)	ounces (oz)
15	½
25	1
50	2
75	3
110	4 (¼lb)
150	5
175	6
200	7
225	8 (½lb)
250	9
275	10
300	11
350	12 (¾lb)
375	13
400	14
425	15
450	16 (1lb)
500	1lb 2oz
680	1½lb
750	1lb 10oz
900	2lb

These quantities are not exact, but they have been calculated to give proportionately correct measurements.

SPOON MEASURES

1 tablespoon	=	3 level teaspoons
1 level tablespoon	=	15ml
1 level teaspoon	=	5ml

If greater accuracy is not required:

1 rounded teaspoon	=	2 level teaspoons
1 heaped teaspoon	=	3 level teaspoons or 1 level tablespoon

LIQUID CONVERSIONS

millilitres (ml)	fluid ounces (fl oz)	US cups
15	½	1 tbsp (level)
30	1	⅛
60	2	¼
90	3	⅜
125	4	½
150	5 (¼ pint)	⅔
175	6	¾
225	8	1
300	10 (½ pint)	1¼
350	12	1½
450	16	2
500	18	2¼
600	20 (1 pint)	2½
900	1½ pints	3¾
1 litre	1¾ pints	1 quart (4 cups)
1.25 litres	2 pints	1¼ quarts
1.5 litres	2½ pints	3 US pints
2 litres	3½ pints	2 quarts

These quantities are not exact, but they have been calculated to give proportionately correct measurements.

REFERENCE INTAKE (RI)

Energy (calories)	2,000
Fat (g)	70
of which saturates (g)	20
Carbohydrate (g)	260
of which total sugars (g)	90
Protein (g)	50
Salt (g)	6

These amounts indicate an adult's daily requirements for a healthy, balanced diet.

GRILLING TIMES: FISH

	minutes each side
Cod (steak)	5–6
Dover sole (fillet)	2–3
Halibut (steak)	5–6
Herring (whole)	4–5
Mackerel (whole)	6–7
Monkfish (steak)	5–6
Plaice (whole)	4–6
Plaice (fillet)	2–3
Salmon (steak)	5–6
Skate	5–6
Tuna (steak)	1–2

Times given for fish weighing approximately 175–225g (6–8oz).

OVEN TEMPERATURES

°C	(fan)	°F	gas	description
110	(90)	225	¼	cool
120/130	(100/110)	250	½	cool
140	(120)	275	1	very low
150	(130)	300	2	very low
160/170	(140/150)	325	3	low to moderate
180	(160)	350	4	moderate
190	(170)	375	5	moderately hot
200	(180)	400	6	hot
220	(200)	425	7	hot
230	(210)	450	8	hot
240	(220)	475	9	very hot

Guide to recommended equivalent settings, not exact conversions. Always refer to your cooker instruction book.

ROASTING TIMES: MEAT*
Set oven temperature to 180°C/160°fan/Gas 4.

	cooking time per 450g/1lb	extra cooking time
Beef		
rare	20 min	20 min
medium	25 min	25 min
well done	30 min	30 min
Lamb		
medium	25 min	25 min
well done	30 min	30 min
Pork		
medium	30 min	30 min
well done	35 min	35 min

Let the cooked meat rest for 5–15 minutes before carving to allow the juices to be reabsorbed and to make carving easier.

STEAMING TIMES: VEGETABLES

	minutes
Asparagus	5–7
Beansprouts	3–4
Beetroot (sliced)	5–7
Broccoli (florets)	5–7
Brussels sprouts	5–7
Cabbage (chopped)	4–6
Carrots (thickly sliced)	5–7
Cauliflower (florets)	5–7
Courgettes (sliced)	3–5
Green beans	5–7
Leeks	5–8
Mangetout peas	3–5
Peas	3–5
Potatoes (cubed)	5–7

Times given are for steaming from when water has started to boil.

ROASTING TIMES: POULTRY*

	oven temperature	cooking time per 450g/1lb	extra cooking time	resting time
Chicken	220°C/200°fan/Gas 7 for 20 min; then 190°C/170°fan/Gas 5	20 min	20 min	15 min
Turkey (stuffed weight)	220°C/200°fan/Gas 7 uncovered for 30 min; then, covered, 190°C/170°fan/Gas 5; then for last 30 min, uncovered, 200°C/180°fan/Gas 6	18 min	18 min	30 min
Duck	230°C/210°fan/Gas 8 for 20 min; then 180°C/160°fan/Gas 4	15 min	—	15 min

*Note that for fan ovens, cooking times are generally reduced by 10 minutes for every hour. These timings and oven temperatures are guidelines – follow instructions on packaging if possible.

How to get your 5 a day

A balanced diet contains at least five different portions of fruit and vegetables a day and a good mix throughout the week.

Sometimes eating healthily can feel like a minefield in the face of so much conflicting advice. Still, we all know eating enough fruit and veg is crucial for good health. It needn't be confusing: at its best, getting your 5 a day can be simple and delicious. Each number below represents 1 of your 5 a day.

RED
Tomato	1
Cherry tomatoes	7
Rhubarb (cooked)	2 tbsp
Strawberries	7
Cherries	14
Pepper	½

ORANGE
Orange	1
Nectarine	1
Apricots	3
Carrots	3 tbsp
Baked Beans	3 tbsp
Sweet potato	1

YELLOW
Banana	1
Grapefruit	½
Pineapple	1 slice
Sweetcorn	3 tbsp
Yellow lentils	3 tbsp
Chickpeas	3 tbsp

GREEN
Apple	1
Melon	1 slice
Lettuce	1 bowl
Peas	3 tbsp
Green beans	4 tbsp
Avocado	½

PURPLE
Plums	2
Blackcurrants	4 tbsp
Sultanas	1 tbsp
Kidney beans	3 tbsp
Beetroot	7 slices
Aubergine	½

WHITE
Leek	1
Cauliflower	8 florets
Mushrooms (chopped)	3 tbsp
Turnip/swede	3 tbsp
Butter beans	3 tbsp
Parsnip	1

EAT THE RAINBOW

Try to choose each portion from a different colour group. Aiming for a colourful plate can be a simple way to get the full range of vitamins and minerals your body needs. And your meals will be beautiful, too!

WHAT COUNTS?

Almost all fruits and vegetables count towards your 5 a day. This includes fresh produce, frozen, tinned and preserved fruits and vegetables.

One portion of your 5 a day…
= 80g of fruit
= 80g of vegetables
= 30g dried fruit

DID YOU KNOW…?

Mixing fruits or vegetables (e.g. 40g banana and 40g strawberries) still counts towards your total as long as each portion adds up to 80g.

Fruit juices and smoothies only count as one portion, no matter how many glasses you drink. The NHS recommends no more than 150ml a day.

Pulses, beans and legumes, like lentils, kidney beans or chickpeas, only count as one portion of your 5 a day, regardless of how many 80g portions you eat.

Potatoes don't count towards your 5 a day because of their high starch content, but they are still a great source of fibre, potassium and B vitamins. However, sweet potatoes do count.

Washing instructions

 TEXTILE CYCLES

Check both the temperature, given by the figure in the tub, and the machine-action, shown by the bar(s) under it. The temperature may be indicated by dots (six for 95°, four for 60°, two for 40° and one for 30°).

 Maximum agitation. Cotton cycle
White cotton or linen articles without special finishes.

 Maximum agitation. Cotton cycle
Cotton or linen articles without special finishes where colours are fast at 60°C.

 Maximum agitation. Cotton cycle
Cotton or linen where colours are fast at 40°C but not at 60°C.

 Medium agitation. Synthetic cycle
Acrylics, acetate or triacetate, including mixtures with wool, polyester and wool blends.

 Minimum agitation. Wool cycle
Wool, including blankets, wool mixed with other fibres, viscose and silk.

 Gentle agitation. Delicates cycle
Silk, acetates and mixed synthetics not colourfast at 40°C.

 Hand wash only
See garment label for further instructions.

 Do not machine or hand wash

 DRY-CLEANING

The letter P or F indicates the cleaning fluids that may be used by your professional dry-cleaner.

 May be dry-cleaned   Do not dry-clean

 BLEACHING

Bleach may be used   Do not bleach

Do not use chlorine bleach

DRYING SYMBOLS

Check the label to see if your garment can be tumble-dried. The label may advise using a reduced heat setting by putting a single dot within the circle. Two dots indicate a higher heat setting.

 May be tumble-dried   Drip dry recommended

 Do not tumble-dry   Dry flat

 Hang dry

IRONING

• The dots inside the iron indicate the temperature setting. One dot represents the coolest setting and three dots are for the hottest temperature. The table (right) is a guide to the temperature to use for specific types of fabric.
• You should always use the setting recommended by the manufacturer. For some materials the advice may be that you iron on the wrong side of the fabric only, so check the label.
• To avoid creases, store your clothes in drawers and wardrobes loosely; don't pack them in.

 Hot (3 dots)
Cotton and linen fabrics.

 Warm (2 dots)
Polyester mixtures and wool.

 Cool (1 dot) Acrylic, nylon, acetate, triacetate, viscose and polyester.

 Do not iron

Stain removal

The most important factor in attacking stains is to act swiftly. The newer the stain, whether greasy, non-greasy, or a combination of the two, the easier it will be to remove without damage.

First and foremost, check what processes and cleaning agents are suitable for the stained item. Wool and silk often need to be treated differently from cotton and synthetics, for example. Always check care labels if possible, and follow what they say.

Likewise, bear in mind that whites may need to be treated differently from coloureds. In any case, always check for colourfastness before soaking.

Biological detergent works well even at low temperatures due to the enzymes it contains.

Whenever you can, use it for stain removal but don't use it, or any other enzyme-based cleaner, on wool or silk. For hand-washing, old or delicate fabrics and baby clothes, use a mild non-biological detergent.

Some of the cleaning agents you will need contain chemicals that are poisonous or flammable. Always read the packaging carefully and store them away from children.

For your safety, work in an area that has plenty of ventilation.

CLEANING KIT

Bicarbonate of soda: Use this – or cornflour or talcum powder – to absorb grease and oil.

Borax: Boosts your detergent's performance.

Detergents: Biological/non-biological/heavy-duty/mild. Liquid detergent is good for oily stains and as a pre-wash treatment.

Eucalyptus oil: Available from major chemists. Good for treating greasy stains.

Glycerine: For treating old stains before washing.

Hydrogen peroxide: Ask your chemist for 3%, which is 10 volume strength (VS). Don't use on wool or silk.

Methylated spirits: From DIY stores. Apply with cotton buds. Don't use on fabric that contains acetate or triacetate.

Pre-wash treatments: Some are for common stains, some are more specific. Follow the manufacturer's instructions.

White distilled vinegar: Use as a solution of 15ml vinegar to 300ml water (3 tsp to ½ pint); or mixed to a paste with bicarbonate of soda.

White spirit: Available from DIY stores. Good for treating paint and grease stains.

PERSONAL

Blood: Soak in cold water with biological detergent or salt; or rub in a paste of bicarb and cold water, leave to dry, brush off. Wash in biological detergent (if appropriate for the fabric).

Make-up: Work in biological liquid detergent; wash as usual.

Perspiration: Sponge with white vinegar, rinse and soak in salt solution or biological detergent. Soften old stains with glycerine. Rinse, wash as usual.

Urine: Rinse in cold water; dab with hydrogen peroxide, or soak in biological detergent; rinse, wash as usual. For pet urine, soak in soda water, blot excess, sponge with salty water, rinse and blot dry. Sprinkle with bicarb, leave for a while, then vacuum.

Vomit: Rinse under running cold water; soak in a sterilising solution, or biological detergent with some disinfectant added; wash as usual.

FOOD AND DRINKS

Chocolate: Rinse in cold water; apply biological detergent and soak overnight if necessary; wash in suitable detergent.

Coffee: Soak in lukewarm water, use a pre-wash treatment and wash in suitable detergent.

Egg: Dab with cold salty water; wash in biological detergent.

Gravy: Soak in cold water with biological detergent; usual wash.

Grease: Cover with bicarb, leave for an hour; brush off.

WHAT TO DO

• Remove any solids with a blunt knife, and blot liquids with white kitchen paper.
• Apply stain remover to a small, unseen area and wait 5–10 minutes. If the fabric reacts, or if in doubt, seek dry-cleaning advice. Avoid treating delicate or expensive fabrics, or those that require dry-cleaning only.

Soak in liquid detergent and wash in water as hot as the fabric allows.

Milk and fruit juice: Rinse under running cold water, then soak in biological detergent and wash in water as hot as the fabric allows.

Oil/salad dressings: Blot and dab with biological liquid detergent; or sprinkle with bicarb, brush off and soak in washing-up liquid. Usual wash.

Tea: Treat as coffee but wash in heavy-duty detergent; or dab with lemon juice, rinse and wash in biological detergent; or pour white vinegar solution, leave for 10 mins and wash.

Tomato sauce: Dab gently with biological liquid detergent and wash as usual; or rinse in cold water, dab with white vinegar, rinse and wash as usual.

Wine, red: Pour soda water over the stain, blot, cover with salt and leave for 30 minutes. Soak in cold water; sponge with biological detergent and wash as usual. On upholstery and carpets, cover with salt, leave to absorb and brush off. Dab with warm water and biological detergent; then with cold water.

Wine, white: Rinse in warm water; dab with biological liquid

• Don't over-soak the fabric with a cleaning agent. To avoid making a ring mark, use a soft, absorbent cloth to apply the cleaning agent and work in a circular motion from the outside inwards. Dab, rather than rub, because rubbing can damage the fabric and it can also spread the stain.

detergent (white vinegar for silk and wool). Rinse and wash as usual. On upholstery and carpets, blot then sponge gently with soapy water (do not rub).

MISCELLANEOUS

Grass: Dab with methylated spirits; rinse with warm soapy water. Use an appropriate pre-wash treatment and then wash in heavy-duty detergent.

Ink (ballpoint or felt tip): Dab with diluted methylated spirits; rinse and sponge with biological detergent; wash as usual. If persistent, treat as rust.

Rust: Dab with lemon juice, cover with salt, leave for at least an hour; rinse; usual wash.

Suntan lotion: Use a pre-wash for greasy stains, or treat with eucalyptus oil or a product for removing hard-water stains. Wash in biological detergent.

Tar: Dab with eucalyptus oil on reverse of fabric; wash in biological detergent in water as hot as fabric allows.

Metric conversions

			To convert	multiply by

Length

			To convert	multiply by
1 millimetre (mm)		= 0.0394in	mm to in	0.0394
1 centimetre (cm)	= 10mm	= 0.394in	cm to in	0.394
1 metre (m)	= 100cm	= 1.09yd	m to yd	1.09
1 kilometre (km)	= 1000m	= 0.621 mile	km to mi	0.621
1 inch (in)		= 2.54cm	in to cm	2.54
1 foot (ft)	= 12in	= 30.5cm	ft to cm	30.5
1 yard (yd)	= 3ft	= 0.914m	yd to m	0.914
1 mile (mi)	= 1760yd	= 1.61km	mi to km	1.61

Area

			To convert	multiply by
1 sq millimetre (mm)		= 0.00155sq in	mm^2 to in^2	0.00155
1 sq centimetre (cm)	= 100sq mm	= 0.155sq in	cm^2 to in^2	0.155
1 sq metre (m)	= 10,000sq cm	= 1.2sq yd	m^2 to yd^2	1.2
1 hectare (ha)	= 10,000sq m	= 2.47a	ha to a	2.47
1 sq kilometre (km)	= 100ha	= 0.386sq mile	km^2 to mi^2	0.386
1 sq inch (in)		= 6.45sq cm	in^2 to cm^2	6.45
1 sq foot (ft)	= 144sq in	= 0.0929sq m	ft^2 to m^2	0.0929
1 sq yard (yd)	= 9sq ft	= 0.836sq m	yd^2 to m^2	0.836
1 acre (a)	= 4840sq yd	= 4047sq m	a to m^2	4047
1 sq mile (mi)	= 640a	= 2.59sq km	mi^2 to km^2	2.59

Volume

			To convert	multiply by
1 cu centimetre (cm)	= 1000cu mm	= 0.0611cu in	cm^3 to in^3	0.0611
1 cu decimetre (dm)	= 1000cu cm	= 0.0353cu ft	dm^3 to ft^3	0.0353
1 cu metre (m)	= 1000cu dm	= 1.31cu yd	m^3 to yd^3	1.31
1 cu inch (in)		= 16.4cu cm	in^3 to cm^3	16.4
1 cu foot (ft)	= 1730cu in	= 28.4cu dm	ft^3 to dm^3	28.4
1 cu yard (yd)	= 27cu ft	= 0.765cu m	yd^3 to m^3	0.765

Capacity

			To convert	multiply by
1 millilitre (ml)		= 0.0352fl oz	ml to fl oz	0.0352
1 centilitre (cl)	= 10ml	= 0.352fl oz	cl to fl oz	0.352
1 litre (l)	= 100cl	= 1.76pt	l to pt	1.76
1 fluid ounce (fl oz)		= 28.4ml	fl oz to ml	28.4
1 gill (gi)	= 5fl oz	= 14.2cl	gi to cl	14.2
1 pint (pt)	= 20fl oz	= 0.568l	pt to l	0.568
1 quart (qt)	= 2pt	= 1.14l	qt to l	1.14
1 gallon (gal)	= 4qt	= 4.55l	gal to l	4.55

Weight

			To convert	multiply by
1 gram (g)	= 1000mg	= 0.0353oz	g to oz	0.0353
1 kilogram (kg)	= 1000g	= 2.2lb	kg to lb	2.2
1 tonne (t)	= 1000kg	= 0.984 ton	tonne to ton	0.984
1 ounce (oz)	= 438 grains	= 28.3g	oz to g	28.3
1 pound (lb)	= 16oz	= 0.454kg	lb to kg	0.454
1 stone (st)	= 14lb	= 6.35kg	st to kg	6.35
1 ton (t)	= 160st	= 1.02 tonne	ton to tonne	1.02

2021

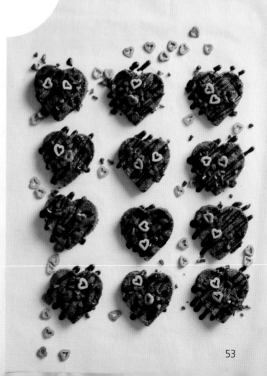

28 Monday

29 Tuesday

30 Wednesday

31 Thursday
New Year's Eve

1 Friday JANUARY 2021
New Year's Day
Bank Holiday, UK

REMINDERS

Saturday 2

Sunday 3

MEDJOOL DATES WITH FETA

Medjool dates 9
Feta cheese 50g (2oz)
Tahini paste 1 tbsp
Extra virgin olive oil 2 tsp
Toasted sesame seeds 2 tsp

1 Slit dates lengthways and remove stones. Thinly slice feta and push a little into each date. Arrange on a serving platter.
2 Whisk tahini with 1 tablespoon water to loosen; season with salt and freshly ground black pepper. Drizzle tahini mixture over dates, then drizzle with oil and scatter over sesame seeds. Serve at room temperature.

TIP Serve as a party canapé or even as a dinner party dessert. They can be prepared a few hours before serving.

Makes 9 • **Time 15 mins**
Calories 100 • Fibre 1.5g • Salt 0.1g • Sugar 0g
Fat 4.8g of which 1.3g is saturated

4 Monday
Bank Holiday, Scotland

5 Tuesday

6 Wednesday
☾ Last quarter
Epiphany

7 Thursday

8 Friday

REMINDERS

Sunday 10

LEEK, BLUE CHEESE & MIXED NUT RISOTTO

Butter 25g (1oz)
Leeks 3, trimmed and thinly sliced
Arborio or risotto rice 200g (7oz)
Dry sherry or vermouth 6 tbsp
Hot vegetable stock 1 litre (1¾ pints)
Long Clawson Shropshire blue cheese or other blue cheese 150g (5oz)
Mixed nuts 50g (2oz), toasted and roughly chopped

1 Melt half the butter in a large pan, add leeks and cook gently for 5 minutes. Cover with a lid and cook for a further 5 minutes. Remove lid, then stir in rice for 1 minute to combine.
2 Pour in sherry and simmer until absorbed. Add half the stock, stir well, and once almost absorbed, stir in half the remaining stock. Continue to add remaining stock while simmering for 10 minutes or until rice softens but retains bite.
3 Remove pan from heat and stir in remaining butter. Cover and leave for 5 minutes. Crumble over two-thirds of cheese and mix in. Spoon into 4 bowls. Crumble over remaining cheese, garnish with nuts and season with freshly ground black pepper.

TIP Some blue cheeses contain animal rennet, so check the label if vegetarian.

Serves 4 • **Time 40 mins**
Calories 503 • Fibre 4.4g • Salt 2g • Sugar 0g
Fat 26g of which 13.1g is saturated

11 Monday

12 Tuesday

13 Wednesday
● New moon

14 Thursday

15 Friday

REMINDERS

Saturday 16

Sunday 17

PIPERADE

Olive oil 1 tbsp
Onions 350g (12oz), peeled and chopped
Green peppers 2, deseeded and sliced
Tomatoes 450g (1lb), chopped
Chopped fresh basil 1 tbsp, plus small
leaves to garnish
Eggs 6
Double cream 4 tbsp
Toasted rustic bread to serve (optional)

1 Heat oil in a frying pan and gently fry
onions until soft but not brown. Add peppers
and cook slowly with onion until soft.
2 Add tomatoes and chopped basil to pan;
season. Cover and simmer for 20 minutes
or until most of the liquid has evaporated.
3 Break eggs into a bowl, add cream and
beat gently with a fork. Pour egg mixture
over vegetables and cook, stirring, until
eggs are scrambled. Divide between
warmed bowls and serve with extra basil
leaves scattered over the top and slices of
toast, if you like.

Serves 4 • **Time 30 mins**
Calories 300 • Fibre 4.7g • Salt 0.4g • Sugar 0.0g
Fat 22g of which 9.4g is saturated

18 Monday

19 Tuesday

20 Wednesday
⟩ First quarter

21 Thursday

22 Friday

REMINDERS

Sunday 24

SPICED CAULIFLOWER WITH CHICKPEAS

Cauliflower 1 medium, trimmed
Chickpeas 400g tin, drained and rinsed
Cumin seeds 1 tsp
Coriander seeds 1 tsp
Garam masala 1 tsp
Turmeric ½ tsp
Rapeseed oil 2 tbsp
Unsweetened coconut yogurt 150g (5oz)
Cucumber ¼, finely diced
Fresh coriander 25g (1oz), roughly chopped
Warmed flatbreads and lemon or lime wedges to serve (optional)

1 Preheat oven to 200°C/180°fan/Gas 6. Chop cauliflower into 4cm (1½in) florets. Put in a large roasting tin with any smaller leaves and chickpeas.
2 Roughly crush cumin and coriander seeds using a pestle and mortar. Mix in garam masala, turmeric and seasoning. Sprinkle spices over vegetables in tin and mix to coat well, then drizzle with oil. Roast for 30-40 minutes until crisp and slightly browned.
3 Meanwhile, mix yogurt, cucumber and most of coriander to make a sauce. Sprinkle remaining coriander over roasted vegetables. Serve with sauce along with warmed flatbreads and lemon or lime wedges, if using.

TIP Use Greek-style yogurt if you prefer.

Serves 4 • Time 50 mins
Calories 300 • Fibre 9.8g • Salt 0.1g • Sugar 0g
Fat 13.9g of which 3.4g is saturated

25 Monday

Burns' Night

26 Tuesday

27 Wednesday

28 Thursday

○ Full moon

29 Friday

REMINDERS

Saturday 30

Sunday 31
Septuagesima Sunday

HAGGIS SAMOSAS

Sunflower oil 1 tbsp
Spring onions 5, trimmed and chopped
Carrots 125g (4½oz), peeled and grated
Haggis 125g (4½oz), crumbled
Cooked white rice 65g (2½oz)
Filo pastry sheets 4 large
Butter 75g (3oz), melted
Cherry tomatoes 150g (5oz), chopped
Sweet chilli sauce 2 tbsp

1 Heat oil in a frying pan and gently fry all but
1 tablespoon spring onions and all carrots for 5
minutes until softened. Leave to cool.
2 In a bowl, mix haggis with rice and cooled
vegetables; season.
3 Cut each pastry sheet into 3 long strips. Working
one strip at a time, brush with melted butter and
place 2 tablespoons of haggis mixture at one end.
4 Fold end of pastry strip over haggis to make a
triangular parcel. Continue folding and wrapping
the parcel down length of pastry strip until you
reach end, folding over as necessary. Cover and
chill, then repeat until you have 12 parcels.
5 Preheat oven to 200°C/180°fan/Gas 6. Line a
baking tray with baking paper and put samosas on
tray. Brush with any remaining melted butter and
bake for 25–30 minutes until crisp and golden.
6 Meanwhile, mix tomatoes with remaining spring
onions and chilli sauce. Put in a bowl, cover and
chill until required. Serve hot samosas with salsa.

Makes 12 • Time 1 hr 30 mins
Calories 144 • Fibre 1.3g • Salt 0.4g • Sugar 1.4g
Fat 8.9g of which 4.2g is saturated

63

1 Monday

2 Tuesday

3 Wednesday

4 Thursday
(Last quarter

5 Friday

REMINDERS

MOROCCAN MEATLOAF WITH APRICOT CHUTNEY

Red onion 1 small, peeled and chopped
White wine vinegar 3 tbsp
Soft dried apricots 250g (9oz), chopped
Orange juice 200ml (7fl oz)
Caster sugar 2 tbsp
Fresh coriander leaves 5 tbsp, chopped
Lean lamb mince 500g (1lb 2oz)
Lean turkey mince 250g (9oz)
Garlic cloves 2, peeled and crushed
White breadcrumbs 40g (1½oz)
Eggs 2 medium, beaten
Ground cumin 2 tsp
Pitted green olives 70g pack, chopped
Cooked rice and salad to serve (optional)

1 To make the chutney, put onion and vinegar in a pan. Add 150g (5oz) apricots, the orange juice and sugar. Heat, stirring, until sugar dissolves. Bring to the boil, cover and simmer for 30 minutes until thick. Leave to cool, then stir in 2 tablespoons coriander; season. Chill, covered, until required.
2 Preheat oven to 180°C/160°fan/Gas 4. Grease a 900g (2lb) loaf tin. Mix all remaining ingredients with remaining apricots and coriander; season.
3 Press mixture into tin, rounding the top. Cover with foil and bake for 45 minutes. Remove foil and cook for 20 minutes more until cooked through. Cover and rest for 15 minutes before removing from tin. Slice and serve with chutney alongside cooked rice and salad, if you like.

Serves 6 • Time 1 hr 45 mins plus standing
Calories 385 • Fibre 5.4g • Salt 0.7g • Sugar 9.3g
Fat 17g of which 6.6g is saturated

65

8   Monday

9   Tuesday

10 Wednesday

11 Thursday
● New moon

12 Friday
Chinese New Year

REMINDERS

BROWNIE HEARTS

Butter 150g (5oz) at room temperature
Light muscovado sugar 75g (3oz)
Vanilla extract 1 tsp
Plain flour 110g (4oz)
Cocoa powder 25g (1oz)
Ground almonds 75g (3oz)
Egg 1 large, yolk only
Dark chocolate 25g (1oz), melted
Freeze-dried crushed raspberries 2 tsp
Edible heart sprinkles 2 tsp
Icing sugar for dusting

1 Preheat oven to 170°C/150°fan/Gas 3
and line a baking sheet with baking paper.
In a bowl, cream butter, sugar and vanilla with
an electric whisk. Sift over flour and cocoa,
stir in ground almonds and mix to crumbs. Stir
in yolk and mix to a soft dough. Spread out to
a 20cm (8in) square on lined baking sheet.
2 Bake for 20 minutes. Cool on the baking
paper on a wire rack. Slide paper onto a
board and cut out heart shapes using a 5cm
(2in) cutter. Transfer to a wire rack.
3 Spoon chocolate into a paper piping bag,
pipe zig-zags over hearts or ice a stripe of
chocolate across each heart. Sprinkle with
crushed raspberries and heart sprinkles; leave
to set. Dust with icing sugar to serve. Keeps
for 2 days in an airtight container.

TIP Use crushed crystallised rose petals or
violets instead of raspberries, if you like.

Makes 16 brownies • Time 45 mins plus cooling
Calories 164 • Fibre 0.6g • Salt 0.1g • Sugar 7.8g
Fat 11.6g of which 5.7g is saturated

15 Monday

16 Tuesday
Shrove Tuesday

17 Wednesday
Ash Wednesday

18 Thursday

19 Friday
) First quarter

REMINDERS

MUSHROOM PANCAKES

Plain flour 110g (4oz) plus 2 tbsp
Egg 1
Milk 700ml (24fl oz)
Vegetable oil for brushing
Butter 75g (3oz)
Mushrooms 450g (1lb) button or mixed, sliced
Mustard ½ tsp
Chopped fresh parsley 2 tbsp
Cheddar 50g (2oz) (optional)
Green salad to serve (optional)

1 For pancakes, sift flour into a bowl and break in egg. Gradually add 125ml (4fl oz) milk, beating to a smooth batter. Pour in another 125ml (4fl oz) milk and beat until smooth.

2 Brush a non-stick frying pan with oil and pour in enough of batter to coat base. Cook until pancake moves freely, flip and cook until golden. Repeat to make 8 pancakes. Keep warm.

3 Melt 50g (2oz) butter in a frying pan over a medium heat and fry mushrooms for 4-5 minutes, until soft and just browning. Remove from pan and keep warm.

4 Melt remaining butter in pan and add 2 tablespoons flour. Cook for 1-2 minutes, then gradually add remaining milk, beating well and allowing to boil between each addition of milk. Simmer for 2 minutes, then stir in mustard, parsley and mushrooms; season.

5 Preheat grill to hot. Divide mushroom mixture between pancakes, and roll up. Arrange on a greased dish, sprinkle with cheese, if using, then grill until golden. Serve with a green salad, if you like.

Serves 4 • Time 30 mins
Calories 360 • Fibre 2.2g • Salt 0.3g • Sugar 0g
Fat 22g of which 12.3g is saturated

22 Monday

23 Tuesday

24 Wednesday

25 Thursday

26 Friday

REMINDERS

Saturday 27
○ Full moon

Sunday 28

ROASTED PARSNIP, PEAR & WENSLEYDALE SALAD

Parsnips 2 medium, peeled and quartered
Chilli oil 1 tbsp plus 2 tsp extra
Honey 1 tsp
Soy sauce 2 tsp
White wine vinegar 1 tsp
Babyleaf salad 50g (2oz)
Ripe pear 1 small, cored and sliced
Mixed nuts 25g (1oz), chopped
Wensleydale cheese 50g (2oz)

1 Preheat oven to 220°C/200°fan/Gas 7 and line a baking tray with baking paper. Coat parsnips with 1 tablespoon oil and roast on tray for 20 minutes or until tender.
2 Mix remaining oil with honey, soy sauce and vinegar to make a dressing.
3 Divide salad between two plates, scatter over roasted parsnips, pear slices and nuts. Drizzle with dressing and crumble over cheese. Serve immediately.

Serves 2 • **Time 30 mins**
Calories 349 • Fibre 6.4g • Salt 1g • Sugar 3g
Fat 23.8g of which 6.7g is saturated

MARCH

1 Monday
St David's Day

2 Tuesday

3 Wednesday

4 Thursday

5 Friday

REMINDERS

Saturday 6
(Last quarter

Sunday 7

CHICKEN & LEEK RAREBIT PIE

Butter 65g (2½oz)
Leek 1 large, trimmed and sliced
Cooked chicken 300g (11oz), cut into bite-sized pieces
Ready-made white sauce 450ml (¾ pint)
Plain flour 1 tbsp
Mustard powder 1 tsp
Stout or beer 6 tbsp
Cheddar 150g (5oz), grated
White bread 3 large slices, toasted
Chopped fresh chives 2 tbsp
Vegetables or salad to serve (optional)

1 Melt 50g (2oz) butter in a frying pan over a medium heat and fry leek for 5 minutes, stirring, until softened. Add chicken and white sauce, bring to the boil, then simmer, stirring, for 10-15 minutes until heated through. Transfer to a 22cm (9in) round ovenproof pie dish, cover and keep warm.
2 Melt remaining butter in a small pan, stir in flour and cook gently for 1 minute. Remove from heat, stir in mustard powder and stout or beer, then heat through, stirring, until thickened. Remove from heat and stir in cheese. Preheat grill to medium-hot.
3 Cut toast into quarters and arrange, overlapping, over chicken. Spread cheese mixture evenly on top. Grill for 7-8 minutes until bubbling. Sprinkle with chives and serve with vegetables or salad, if you like.

Serves 4 • **Time 45 mins**
Calories 619 • Fibre 2.3g • Salt 1.4g • Sugar 0.2g
Fat 40.1g of which 22.8g is saturated

73

MARCH

8   Monday

9   Tuesday

10 Wednesday

11 Thursday

12 Friday

REMINDERS

Saturday 13
● New moon

Sunday 14
Mothering Sunday

ALMOND & RASPBERRY CELEBRATION CAKE

Butter 350g (12oz), softened
Caster sugar 350g (12oz)
Eggs 6
Vanilla extract 2 tsp
Almond extract 1 tsp
Self-raising flour 175g (6oz)
Ground almonds 175g (6oz)
Ready-made vanilla butter icing 2 x 400g tubs
Raspberries 200g punnet plus extra to decorate
Sugar shimmer and sugar flowers to decorate

1 Preheat oven to 180°C/160°fan/Gas 4. Grease and line 3 x18cm (7in) sandwich tins. Cream butter and sugar until light and fluffy.
2 Add eggs one at a time, beating well after each addition.
3 Mix in vanilla and almond extracts, then fold in flour and ground almonds.
4 Divide mixture between prepared tins. Bake for 35 minutes or until a skewer inserted comes out clean. Leave to cool on a wire rack.
5 Fix bottom layer to a board with a pat of icing. Spread top with icing and scatter over raspberries. Add second layer and repeat with icing and raspberries. Place on third layer (inverted for a flat top). Using a palette knife, put remaining icing on top; spread to edges. Continue to push icing down sides, turning, until cake is covered. Decorate with extra raspberries, sugar shimmer and sugar flowers.

Serves 10–12 • **Time 1¼ hrs**
Calories 779 • Fibre 1.1g • Salt 0.4g • Sugar 75.1g
Fat 45.7g of which 22.9g is saturated

75

15 Monday

16 Tuesday

17 Wednesday
St Patrick's Day
Bank Holiday, Northern Ireland

18 Thursday

19 Friday

REMINDERS

Saturday 20
Vernal equinox
Spring begins

Sunday 21
) First quarter

MADRAS BEEF CURRY

Rapeseed or sunflower oil 2 tbsp
Onions 2 medium, peeled and sliced
Garlic cloves 2, peeled and crushed
Root ginger 2.5cm (1in) piece, peeled and finely chopped
Ground turmeric 1 tsp
Garam masala 2 tsp
Cumin seeds 1 tsp, crushed
Dried chilli flakes 1 tsp
Chuck or braising steak 680g (1½lb), cut into 2.5cm (1in) cubes
Chopped tomatoes 400g tin
Hot beef stock 400ml (14fl oz)
Natural yogurt to serve (optional)
Fresh coriander small handful, chopped, to garnish (optional)
Rice, naan bread and chutneys to serve (optional)

1 Heat oil in a 1.2 litre (2 pint) flameproof, lidded casserole dish and fry onions, garlic, ginger, spices and chilli for 3-4 minutes, stirring occasionally.
2 Add steak for 2-3 minutes until lightly coloured.
3 Add tomatoes and stock. Bring to boil, cover and cook for 2-2½ hours on the hob, stirring occasionally. Alternatively, cook in a preheated oven at 180°C/160°fan/Gas 4 until beef is tender. Season if required.
4 Serve alongside yogurt, garnish with coriander and accompany with rice, naan and chutneys.

Serves 6 • **Time 3 hrs**
Calories 251 • Fibre 2g • Salt 0.8g • Sugar 0g
Fat 13.9g of which 4.6g is saturated

77

22 Monday

23 Tuesday

24 Wednesday

25 Thursday

26 Friday

REMINDERS

Saturday 27

Don't forget to put your clocks forward 1 hour tonight
(t.b.c. dependent on Government ruling)

Sunday 28

○ Full moon
Palm Sunday

HAKE WITH CRUNCHY SEAWEED CRUMB

Panko breadcrumbs 3 tbsp
Aonori seaweed 1½ tbsp
Sesame oil 3 tsp
Toasted sesame seeds 2 tsp
Rapeseed oil 2 tsp
Hake fillets 2 x 150g (5oz)
Japanese rice vinegar 3 tsp
Buckwheat soba noodles 110g (4oz)
Soy sauce 1 tsp
Spring onions 2, trimmed and finely sliced
Steamed broccoli to serve (optional)

1 Preheat oven to 200°C/180°fan/Gas 6. Toast breadcrumbs in an ovenproof frying pan for 1-2 minutes; tip into a bowl. Stir in seaweed, 1 teaspoon each sesame oil and sesame seeds.
2 Reheat frying pan and add rapeseed oil. Season fish and place, skin-side down, in pan. Spoon 1 teaspoon vinegar over each fillet, then sprinkle with seaweed mixture. Cook for 3 minutes, put in oven and cook for 3-4 minutes until golden on top.
3 Meanwhile, cook noodles in boiling water for 5 minutes, drain and rinse in cold water. Mix remaining sesame oil, seeds and vinegar with soy sauce and spring onions in pan. Add noodles and heat through. Divide between warmed plates, top with fish and serve with broccoli, if using.

TIP Aonori is a fragrant Japanese seaweed, available chopped and dried in small tubs.

Serves 2 • Time 20 mins
Calories 484 • Fibre 3.1g • Salt 1.8g • Sugar 0g
Fat 14.1g of which 1.9g is saturated

79

29 Monday

30 Tuesday

31 Wednesday

1 Thursday APRIL

2 Friday
Good Friday
Bank Holiday, UK

REMINDERS

EASTER LEMON AND WHITE CHOCOLATE SLICE

Plain shortbread biscuits 200g (7oz)
Desiccated coconut 50g (2oz)
Butter 75g (3oz), melted
Lemon curd 325g jar
Cream cheese 300g (11oz)
White cooking chocolate 100g bar, melted

1 Line a 20cm (8in) square tin with baking paper. Break biscuits into bowl of a food processor, add coconut and butter and whizz until crumbs stick together. Press mixture into base of tin. Chill for 10-15 minutes until firm.
2 Meanwhile, make the topping. Set aside 4 tablespoons of lemon curd. Put cheese, remaining curd and chocolate in clean food processor and whizz until smooth. Spread topping over biscuit base. Dot reserved curd over top and swirl with a skewer to create a marbled effect. Chill overnight to set.
3 Cut into 12 fingers to serve. It will keep for up to 4 days in the fridge.

TIPS This is a soft-set cheesecake. If you prefer a firmer cheesecake, add an extra 50g (2oz) white chocolate. Sprinkle with crushed mini eggs, if you like.

Serves 12 • Time 20 mins plus chilling
Calories 402 • Fibre 1.4g • Salt 0.4g • Sugar 32.4g
Fat 25.4g of which 16.1g is saturated

81

5   Monday

Easter Monday
Bank Holiday, England, Wales, Northern Ireland

6   Tuesday

7   Wednesday

8   Thursday

9   Friday

REMINDERS

Saturday 10

Sunday 11
Low Sunday

MINT-MARINATED LAMB
WITH BLUEBERRY GRAVY

Olive oil 3 tbsp
Garlic cloves 3 large, peeled and finely chopped
Fresh mint leaves 2 tsp, roughly chopped
Lemon 1, finely grated zest
Lamb leg joint 1.3kg (3lb)
Blueberries 150g (5oz), lightly crushed
Plain flour 1 tbsp
Hot lamb stock 300ml (½ pint)
Red wine 6 tbsp
Redcurrant jelly 1 tbsp
Seasonal vegetables to serve

1 Preheat oven to 180°C/160°fan/Gas 4. Put oil, garlic, mint and zest in a large dish. Place joint on a board, make several cuts over surface and season. Roll joint in mint mixture, stuffing into cuts.
2 Place joint on a rack in a roasting tin and roast for the preferred calculated cooking time (see page 47), basting occasionally. 15 minutes before end of cooking time, brush with half the berries.
3 Remove joint from oven, cover with foil, place on a carving board and rest for 10-15 minutes.
4 For gravy, spoon off excess fat from the tin. Place tin over medium heat, sprinkle over flour and whisk. Add a little stock and whisk again, scraping base of pan. Add wine, jelly, remaining stock and berries. Simmer, stirring occasionally, for 8-10 minutes. Strain before serving.
5 Carve lamb and serve with seasonal vegetables and blueberry gravy.

Serves 6 • **Time 1¾ hrs**
Calories 452 • Fibre 0.8g • Salt 0.6g • Sugar 1.6g
Fat 25.2g of which 7.9g is saturated

12 Monday

● New moon

13 Tuesday

14 Wednesday

15 Thursday

16 Friday

REMINDERS

FRAGRANT BAKED RICE PUDDING

Short grain rice 110g (4oz)
Milk 450ml (¾ pint)
Double cream 100ml (3½fl oz)
Caster sugar 2 tbsp
Vanilla pod 1, split
Cinnamon stick 1
Cardamom pod 1, split
Clear honey 1 tbsp
Rosewater or orange blossom water few drops
Toasted flaked almonds 3 tbsp
Pomegranate seeds 50g (2oz)

1 Preheat oven to 150°C/130°fan/Gas 2. Rinse and drain rice, then spread evenly over 1.2 litre (2 pint) shallow baking dish.
2 Pour over milk and cream, stir in sugar and push in vanilla, cinnamon and cardamom. Cover with foil and bake for 1½ hours. Stir pudding, re-cover and cook for a further 30-45 minutes until rice is tender, most of liquid has been absorbed and loosely creamy in consistency.
3 Remove and discard spices. Stir in honey, sprinkle with rosewater or orange blossom water and rest, loosely covered, for 30 minutes.
4 Serve warm or leave to cool completely, then chill until required. Serve in small portions sprinkled with almonds and pomegranate seeds.

Serves 6 • Time 2½ hrs plus resting
Calories 255 • Fibre 0.6g • Salt 0.1g • Sugar 10g
Fat 13.2g of which 6.6g is saturated

85

19 Monday

20 Tuesday
) First quarter

21 Wednesday

22 Thursday

23 Friday

St George's Day

REMINDERS

Saturday 24

Sunday 25

SLOW SPICED OX STEW

Rapeseed oil 2 tbsp
Plain flour 2 rounded tbsp
Ox cheeks 4
Onions 2, peeled and each cut into 6 wedges
Carrots 2 large, peeled and cut into 1cm (½in) slices
Celery 2 sticks, cut into thick slices
Mandarin or satsuma 1, finely grated zest
Thyme 4 sprigs
Bay leaves 2
Star anise 2
Pitted dried dates 6, halved
Peeled plum tomatoes 400g tin
Beef stock pots or stock cubes 2
Mashed potato and broccoli to serve (optional)

1 Preheat oven to 150°C/130°fan/Gas 2. Heat
1 tablespoon oil in a lidded, flameproof casserole dish.
Season flour and use to coat ox cheeks. Brown in oil,
2 at a time, for 2 minutes each side. Remove and drain.
2 Add remaining oil to dish with onions, carrots
and celery. Stir, cover and cook over a low heat for
5 minutes, stirring occasionally. Stir in any leftover
flour, the zest, thyme, bay, star anise and dates.
3 Return meat to dish, add tomatoes and stock and
pour over enough boiling water to cover meat. Bring to
boil on hob, then cover and cook in oven for 4 hours.
4 Lift ox cheeks from dish; set aside, covered. Put dish
on hob over a medium heat for 10 minutes or until
sauce is thickened. Pull meat into large chunks, return
to sauce and remove bay and thyme. Serve stew with
mashed potato and broccoli, if you like.

Serves 8 • Time 4½ hours
Calories 340 • Fibre 3g • Salt 1.1g • Sugar 0.9g
Fat 12.4g of which 4.1g is saturated

26 Monday

27 Tuesday
○ Full moon

28 Wednesday

29 Thursday

30 Friday

REMINDERS

Saturday 1

Sunday 2

PEA & HAM QUICHE

Ready-rolled shortcrust pastry 375g (13oz)
Eggs 4, beaten
Crème fraîche 250ml (8fl oz)
Frozen peas 110g (4oz), defrosted
Spring onions 3, trimmed and finely chopped
Ham 250g (9oz), chopped into chunks
Double Gloucester cheese 75g (3oz), grated
Mixed leaf salad to serve (optional)

1 Preheat oven to 200°C/180°fan/Gas 6. Fold pastry in half and roll out until a little larger than a 23cm (9in) fluted flan tin. Lift pastry over the rolling pin and drape over base of tin, pressing it in place up the flutes. Trim edges of pastry with scissors so it sits a little above top of the tin. Prick base of pastry, then chill for 15 minutes.
2 Line pastry case with non-stick baking paper and baking beans and bake for 15 minutes.
3 Meanwhile, in a jug, mix eggs and crème fraîche; season well.
4 Remove paper and beans from pastry case and reduce oven temperature to 180°C/160°fan/ Gas 4. Pour in creamy mixture and then evenly sprinkle over peas, spring onions, ham and grated cheese.
5 Return quiche to the oven and bake for 25–30 minutes until topping is just set and golden. Serve with a mixed leaf salad, if you like.

Serves 6 • Time 1 hr
Calories 603 • Fibre 3.2g • Salt 1.6g • Sugar 0g
Fat 45.8g of which 22.8g is saturated

3 Monday

(Last quarter
Bank Holiday, UK

4 Tuesday

5 Wednesday

6 Thursday

7 Friday

REMINDERS

Saturday 8

Sunday 9
Rogation Sunday

BLUEBERRY & ORANGE LOAF

Self-raising flour 350g (12oz)
Caster sugar 75g (3oz)
Blueberries 200g (7oz)
Oranges 2, finely grated zest and juice
Milk 4-6 tbsp
Eggs 3
Butter 75g (3oz), melted
Demerara sugar 1-2 tbsp

1 Preheat the oven to 160°C/140°fan/Gas 3. Butter a 900g (2lb) loaf tin and line with baking paper.
2 Sift flour into a large bowl and stir in caster sugar, blueberries and orange zest.
3 Pour orange juice into a measuring jug and make up to 150ml (¼ pint) with milk. Beat in eggs and butter, then pour this into the flour mixture and mix until just combined. Spoon the mixture into loaf tin and sprinkle demerara sugar over the top.
4 Bake for 1-1¼ hours until risen and firm to the touch and a skewer inserted into the centre of the loaf comes out clean.
5 Leave to cool in the tin for 10 minutes, then transfer to a wire rack to cool completely. Cut into slices to serve.

Serves 8 • Time 1½ hrs
Calories 315 • Fibre 2.2g • Salt 0.5g • Sugar 11.9g
Fat 10.6g of which 5.7g is saturated

10 Monday

11 Tuesday
● New moon

12 Wednesday

13 Thursday
Ascension Day
Holy Thursday

14 Friday

REMINDERS

Saturday 15

Sunday 16

SEARED SALMON WITH QUICK-PICKLED VEG

Rice wine vinegar 4 tbsp
Sesame oil 3 tbsp
Mirin 2 tbsp
Sake or dry sherry 1 tbsp
Soy sauce 1 tbsp
Finely grated fresh ginger 1 tbsp
Garlic 1 clove, grated
Salmon tail fillets 2, 110g (4oz) each
Caster sugar 1 tsp
Fish sauce 1 tsp
Carrot 1, peeled and julienned
Cucumber ½, cored and julienned
Radishes 5, trimmed and thinly sliced
Salad leaves 60g (2½oz)
Avocado 1, peeled, stoned and thinly sliced
Toasted sesame seeds 1 tbsp

1 Whisk 2 tablespoons each of vinegar and
sesame oil with mirin, sake or sherry and soy sauce
in a shallow, heatproof dish. Add ginger, garlic and
salmon, skin-side up. Marinate for 20-30 minutes.
2 In a large bowl, mix remaining vinegar with
sugar and fish sauce. Stir in carrot, cucumber
and radishes, and leave to pickle for 20 minutes,
stirring occasionally. Preheat grill to hot.
3 Put salmon dish under hot grill for 5-6 minutes.
4 Arrange salad and avocado on large plates. Pile
pickled vegetables on top, then flake over hot
salmon. Drizzle with leftover pickling juice and
remaining sesame oil. Garnish with sesame seeds.

Serves 2 • **Time 40 mins**
Calories 537 • Fibre 5.3g • Salt 1.9g • Sugar 7.2g
Fat 38g of which 7.1g is saturated

93

17 Monday

18 Tuesday

19 Wednesday
) First quarter

20 Thursday

21 Friday

REMINDERS

Saturday 22

Sunday 23
Whit Sunday
Pentecost

LEMON MERINGUE CLOUD CAKE

Eggs 6 large, separated
Caster sugar 100g (3½oz)
Plain flour 150g (5oz)
Baking powder 1 tsp
Lemon 1 small, finely grated zest and juice
Whipping cream 300ml (½ pint)
Lemon curd 200g (7oz)
Mini meringues 16

1 Preheat oven to 170°C/150°fan/Gas 3. Grease and line 3 x 18cm (7in) round Victoria cake tins. In a bowl, whisk egg yolks and sugar for 5 minutes until pale, thick and creamy.
2 Sift flour and baking powder into bowl, add zest and mix. In another bowl, whisk egg whites to soft peaks and gently fold into batter until combined.
3 Divide batter between tins, smooth tops and bake for 20 minutes until risen and golden. Cool in tins for 5 minutes, then cool on a wire rack.
4 Just before serving, whip cream to peaks. Thin curd with 4-5 tsp lemon juice. Set aside 10 whole meringues; crush the remaining six.
5 Place a sponge on a serving plate and spread with a third of whipped cream. Drizzle with a third of curd and scatter over half of crushed meringues. Place another sponge on top and repeat layers of cream, curd and meringue. Top with final sponge. Spread with remaining cream, drizzle over curd and marble into cream. Decorate with whole meringues. Serve within 30 minutes.

Serves 8-10 • Time 50 mins plus cooling
Calories 329 • Fibre 0.7g • Salt 0.3g • Sugar 23.4g
Fat 16.5g of which 8.8g is saturated

95

24 Monday

25 Tuesday

26 Wednesday
○ Full moon

27 Thursday

28 Friday

REMINDERS

Saturday 29

MINI CHEESY PEASY PIES

Large soft flour tortillas 4
Cooked peas and sweetcorn 200g (7oz)
Spring onions 2, trimmed and chopped
Cheddar 110g (4oz), grated
Eggs 3 medium, beaten
Whole milk 200ml (7fl oz)
Cherry tomatoes 6, halved
Salad or vegetable batons to serve
(optional)

1 Preheat oven to 180°C/160°fan/Gas 4.
Grease a 12-hole muffin or cupcake tin. Cut
out 3 x 12cm (5in) circles from each tortilla
using a cutter or saucer; carefully fold and
press each circle into the tins to make cases.
2 Mix peas, sweetcorn, spring onions and
cheese and spoon into each case.
3 In a jug, beat eggs and milk together;
season. Pour into each case and top each
with a halved cherry tomato. Bake for 25
minutes or until set. Cool for 15 minutes to
firm up before easing out with a knife. Serve
warm or cold with salad or vegetable batons,
if you like.

TIP Replace some of the pea mixture with
chopped ham or chicken for a meaty version.

Makes 12 pies • Time 45 mins
Calories 165 • Fibre 1.8g • Salt 1g • Sugar 0g
Fat 7.1g of which 3.6g is saturated

97

31 Monday
Bank Holiday, UK

1 Tuesday JUNE

2 Wednesday
(Last quarter

3 Thursday
Corpus Christi

4 Friday

REMINDERS

Saturday   5

Sunday   6

LIME & GINGER ICE CREAM WITH CHOCOLATE SAUCE

Condensed milk 397g tin
Double cream 300ml (½ pint)
Unwaxed limes 3, finely grated zest and juice
Stem ginger 5 balls, roughly chopped plus 1 ball, finely chopped
Stem ginger syrup 5 tbsp
Milk 5-6 tbsp
Dark chocolate 100g bar, broken into chunks

1 Put 175g (6oz) condensed milk, cream, zest and juice from 2 limes and roughly chopped ginger in a food processor with a pinch of salt. Whizz until mixture thickens, then pour into a 1 litre (1¾ pints) plastic container and freeze for at least 6 hours or overnight.
2 To make the sauce, warm remaining condensed milk, finely chopped ginger, ginger syrup and milk in a pan. Add chocolate chunks, stirring until they melt. Stir in remaining lime zest and juice and beat until combined.
3 Place 2 scoops of ice cream in each bowl and spoon over hot chocolate sauce. It will set on the ice cream.

Serves 8 • Time 20 mins plus freezing
Calories 453 • Fibre 0.5g • Salt 0.2g • Sugar 38.9g
Fat 27.9g of which 17.2g is saturated

99

7 Monday

8 Tuesday

9 Wednesday

10 Thursday
● New moon

11 Friday

REMINDERS

Saturday 12

Sunday 13

GARLICKY GREEN VEGETABLE PASTA

Dried tagliatelle 300g (11oz)
Fine green beans 110g (4oz), trimmed and halved
Broccoli 110g (4oz), broken into small florets
Butter 25g (1oz)
Courgette 1 large, diced
Soft cheese with garlic and herbs 250g tub
Milk 4 tbsp
Toasted pine nuts 25g (1oz) (optional)

1 Bring a large saucepan of salted water to the boil and cook tagliatelle according to the packet's instructions. Add green beans and broccoli during last 5 minutes of cooking. Drain and return to the pan.
2 Meanwhile, melt butter in a frying pan over a medium-low heat and fry courgette for 4-5 minutes until just softened. Add soft cheese and milk to the pan and gently stir in until melted. Season to taste.
3 To serve, toss pasta with sauce and pile into warmed serving bowls. Sprinkle each portion with pine nuts, if using.

Serves 4 • **Time 15 mins**
Calories 484 • Fibre 6.2g • Salt 0.4g • Sugar 0g
Fat 22g of which 13.5g is saturated

101

14 Monday

15 Tuesday

16 Wednesday

17 Thursday

18 Friday
) First quarter

REMINDERS

PISTACHIO & MARSALA FRUIT SALAD

Strawberries 200g (7oz)
Ripe mangoes 2, stone removed
Ripe peaches 2, stone removed
Caster sugar 1–2 tsp, for sprinkling
Marsala wine, sherry or rose water 4 tbsp
Shelled pistachios 50g (2oz)

1 Hull and finely slice strawberries. Peel and finely slice mangoes. Finely slice peaches. Place fruit into individual serving bowls. Sprinkle a little sugar over each portion.
2 Pour 1 tablespoon Marsala, sherry or rose water over each portion.
3 Toast pistachios until lightly browned and aromatic, then finely chop and sprinkle over each serving.

Serves 4 • Time 15 mins
Calories 173 • Fibre 6.1g • Salt 0.2g • Sugar 2.5g
Fat 7.4g of which 1g is saturated

103

21 Monday
Summer solstice
Summer begins

22 Tuesday

23 Wednesday

24 Thursday
○ Full moon

25 Friday

REMINDERS

Sunday 27

SPICY BEEF & CHEESE FLATBREADS

Rapeseed oil 1 tbsp
Onion 1 small, peeled and finely chopped
Minced beef 225g (8oz)
Garlic 1 clove, peeled and grated
Ras-el-hanout 1 tsp
Dried chilli flakes generous pinch
Large flatbreads or tortillas 3
Toasted pine nuts 3 tbsp
Courgette 1, coarsely grated
Mature Cheddar 110g (4oz), coarsely grated
Green chilli 1, deseeded and thinly sliced
Rocket or baby basil leaves and lemon wedges to serve (optional)

1 Heat oil in a frying pan and add onion, beef, garlic, ras-el-hanout and chilli flakes; season. Fry for 10 minutes, breaking up any lumps of meat with a spoon.
2 Meanwhile, heat each flatbread in a large, heated frying pan for 1 minute each side. Spoon meat into middle of each flatbread. Sprinkle over most of pine nuts, top with courgette and cheese and fold in a crescent shape to enclose filling.
3 Cook flatbreads for 3 minutes each side over a medium heat until golden and cheese has melted. Transfer to a board and cut each into 3 wedges. Garnish with remaining pine nuts and chilli. Serve with leaves and lemon wedges, if liked.

TIP Cook 2 filled flatbreads in a large pan and 1 in a smaller pan so they are ready at the same time.

Serves 2–3 • Time 30 mins
Calories 743 • Fibre 4.8g • Salt 1.2g • Sugar 0g
Fat 47.1g of which 16.9g is saturated

28 Monday

29 Tuesday

30 Wednesday

1 Thursday JULY
(Last quarter

2 Friday

REMINDERS

Saturday   3

Sunday   4

ROLLED BELLY PORK WITH SAGE & APPLE

Belly pork 1.25-1.5kg (about 3½lb)
Onion 1 small, peeled and finely chopped
Cooking apple 1 small, peeled, cored and finely chopped
Chopped fresh sage 2-3 tbsp
Olive oil 1 tbsp
Sea salt flakes 1-2 tbsp
Roast potatoes, carrots, parsnips and gravy to serve (optional)

1 Preheat oven to 220°C/200°fan/Gas 7. Score rind of the pork with parallel lines about 1cm (½in) apart, using a sharp knife.
2 In a bowl, mix onion, apple and sage; season.
3 Place the meat rind-side down on a board; season. Place the onion mixture on top, pressing down firmly, then roll the pork up as tightly as possible, securing with kitchen string.
4 Place the pork in a roasting tin and rub the rind with oil, then sea salt. Put in the oven and cook for 30 minutes.
5 Reduce oven to 150°C/130°fan/Gas 2 and continue roasting for a further 3 hours or until meat is tender and the skin crisp. If the skin isn't crisp, turn the oven back up to 220°C/200°fan/Gas 7 and cook for a further 30 minutes.
6 Leave the meat to rest for 10 minutes before carving. Serve hot with roast potatoes, carrots, parsnips and gravy, if you like.

Serves 6 • **Time 4 hrs**
Calories 565 • Fibre 0.5g • Salt 1.2g • Sugar 0g
Fat 44g of which 15.5g is saturated

107

5   Monday

6   Tuesday

7   Wednesday

8   Thursday

9   Friday

REMINDERS

Saturday 10
● New moon

Sunday 11

ALL-IN-ONE CHICKEN SUPPER

Olive oil 2 tbsp
Chicken thighs 8, excess skin trimmed
Diced chorizo 2 x 60g packs
Red Romano peppers 2, halved, deseeded and cut into large chunks
Red onions 2, peeled and sliced
Small new potatoes 450g (1lb)
Dried chilli flakes 1 tsp (optional)
Garlic 2-4 large cloves, peeled and grated
Sherry vinegar 2 tbsp
Rosemary 2 sprigs
Greens to serve (optional)

1 Preheat oven to 190°C/170°fan/Gas 5.
Put a large roasting tin in the oven. Heat
1 tablespoon oil in a large frying pan and
brown chicken, skin-side down, for 5
minutes, then turn and cook for 2 minutes.
2 Meanwhile, mix chorizo, pepper chunks,
onions, potatoes, chilli (if using), garlic,
vinegar, rosemary and seasoning in roasting
tin. Put chicken thighs, skin-side up, on top.
Drizzle over pan juices and remaining oil.
3 Bake for 45 minutes until cooked through.
Serve with greens, if you like.

TIPS Add slices of fennel for extra flavour.
Use orange juice instead of sherry vinegar, if
you prefer.

Serves 4–6 • Time 1 hr
Calories 329 • Fibre 3.3g • Salt 1g • Sugar 0g
Fat 14.2g of which 4.1g is saturated

12 Monday
Bank Holiday, Northern Ireland

13 Tuesday

14 Wednesday

15 Thursday

16 Friday

REMINDERS

Saturday 17

) First quarter

Sunday 18

PIMM'S CELEBRATION CAKE

Unsalted butter 300g (11oz), softened
Caster sugar 425g (15oz)
Eggs 5 medium
Plain flour 450g (1lb)
Baking powder 1 tbsp
Lemonade 200ml (7fl oz)
Pimm's 250ml (9fl oz)
Double cream 350ml (12fl oz)
Fresh mixed berries 525g (1lb 3oz), halved if large
Soft-set raspberry or strawberry jam 200g (7oz)
Sliced cucumber and mint leaves to decorate

1 Preheat oven to 180°C/160°fan/Gas 4. Grease and
line 2 x 20cm (8in) round, deep cake tins. Put butter in
a bowl with 300g (11oz) sugar and beat until pale and
creamy. Beat in eggs with a little flour.
2 Sift over remaining flour and baking powder and stir
in 150ml (5fl oz) lemonade. Divide between tins. Bake
for 50-60 minutes until risen and golden.
3 Meanwhile, put 200ml (7fl oz) Pimm's and
remaining sugar in a pan. Heat gently, stirring, until
sugar dissolves, then increase heat and boil for 4-5
minutes until lightly syrupy; set aside.
4 Skewer cooked cakes; spoon over syrup. Cool in tins,
then remove and slice horizontally for 4 layers.
5 Whip cream to soft peaks, then beat in remaining
Pimm's and lemonade. Place one layer on a plate and
spread with a quarter cream. Sprinkle with a quarter
berries and drizzle over a third jam.
6 Lay another layer on top and repeat layers, piling
top with remaining cream and berries. Garnish with
cucumber and mint. Serve within 1 hour.

Serves 16 • Time 1 hr 50 mins plus cooling
Calories 544 • Fibre 2.4g • Salt 0.2g • Sugar 33.6g
Fat 29.1g of which 17.6g is saturated

111

19 Monday

20 Tuesday

21 Wednesday

22 Thursday

23 Friday

REMINDERS

Saturday 24
○ Full moon

Sunday 25

FIRE-COOKED VEGETABLES

Baby potatoes 12 small, scrubbed
Red pepper 1 large, deseeded and cut into
bite-sized pieces
Baby corn 12
Spring onions 6, trimmed and cut into 5cm
(2in) lengths
Sunflower oil 3 tbsp
Sesame oil 2 tsp
Sweet chilli sauce 4 tbsp
Little Gem lettuces 2 large, trimmed and
quartered lengthwise
Barbecued meats to serve (optional)

1 Heat the barbecue. Meanwhile, put potatoes
in a small pan, cover with water, add a pinch salt
and bring to boil. Cook for 7-8 minutes until just
tender but not soft. Drain and leave to cool.
2 Bring another pan of water to boil and cook
pepper and baby corn for 3-4 minutes until just
tender but not soft. Drain and cool.
3 Thread potatoes, peppers and spring onions
onto 4 long skewers, cover and chill until ready to
cook. Arrange corn on a piece of foil with edges
folded up and chill until ready to cook.
4 Mix oils with chilli sauce and brush over
vegetable skewers and the cut side of lettuce
halves. Cook the skewers over hot barbecue
coals, turning and basting frequently, for 4-5
minutes until lightly charred and tender. Cook
corn on foil for 4-5 minutes. Cook lettuce for
1-2 minutes. Serve immediately to accompany
barbecued meats, if you like.

Serves 4 • Time 40 mins plus cooling
Calories 225 • Fibre 3.9g • Salt 2.4g • Sugar 1.9g
Fat 14.3g of which 1.9g is saturated

113

26 Monday

27 Tuesday

28 Wednesday

29 Thursday

30 Friday

REMINDERS

Saturday 31
(Last quarter

AUGUST Sunday 1

PINEAPPLE WITH HOT PASSION RUM SAUCE

Passion fruit 3, halved
Dark or golden rum 1-2 tbsp
Light muscovado sugar 3 tbsp
Finely chopped deseeded red chilli 1 tsp
Pineapple 1 small, topped, tailed and skin removed
Chopped fresh mint 1 tbsp (optional)
Vanilla ice cream to serve (optional)

1 Push pulp of 2 passion fruit through a sieve into a small pan, discarding the seeds. Add pulp and seeds from third passion fruit, rum and 1 tablespoon sugar. Simmer for 2 minutes, stirring, until syrupy. Add chilli; leave to cool.
2 Cut pineapple into 6 slices, remove and discard the core. Put remaining sugar on a plate and dip fruit in sugar to coat.
3 Heat a griddle until hot. Griddle pineapple for 1-2 minutes each side until caramelised.
4 Divide between plates. Stir mint into sauce, if using, and spoon over pineapple. Serve with a scoop of vanilla ice cream, if you like.

TIP Use a small round cutter or melon baller to remove pineapple core.

Serves 2 • Time 20 mins
Calories 204 • Fibre 3g • Salt 0g • Sugar 30g
Fat 0.3g of which 0g is saturated

115

2   Monday
Bank Holiday, Scotland

3   Tuesday

4   Wednesday

5   Thursday

6   Friday

REMINDERS

Saturday 7

Sunday 8
● New moon

QUICK CURRANT JAM

Blackcurrants 500g (1lb 2oz), stalks removed
Granulated sugar 750g (1lb 10oz)
Vanilla extract ¼ tsp
Lemon 1, juice only
Liquid pectin 125ml (4fl oz)

1 Remove blackcurrants from stalks, then put in a pan with sugar, vanilla and lemon juice. Stir briefly, then leave in a warm place for 15 minutes until softened.
2 Place on the hob and bring slowly to the boil until sugar is completely dissolved. Stir briefly, then bubble gently for 5 minutes.
3 Remove from the heat, pour in pectin, bring back to the boil and bubble for a further 5 minutes. Leave to cool.
4 While jam cools, sterilise jars. When jam has cooled slightly, stir to redistribute fruit and spoon carefully into sterilised jars. Cool, then cover with waxed circles and a lid. The jam will keep in the fridge for 2-3 weeks.

TIP Liquid glucose can be used as a substitute for liquid pectin.

Makes 1kg (about 2 jars) • **Time 40 mins**
Calories 36 • Fibre 0.3g • Salt 0g • Sugar 9.2g
Fat 0g of which 0g is saturated

117

9 Monday

10 Tuesday

11 Wednesday

12 Thursday

13 Friday

REMINDERS

KEEMA SCOTCH EGGS

Eggs 5
Lamb mince 450g (1lb)
Garlic cloves 2, peeled and finely chopped
Root ginger 2.5cm (1in) piece, peeled and finely chopped
Small green chilli 1, deseeded and finely chopped
Curry paste 2 tbsp
Frozen peas 50g (2oz), thawed and mashed
Fresh coriander large handful, freshly chopped
Plain flour 50g (2oz)
Fresh or dried breadcrumbs 75g (3oz)
Sweet chilli mayonnaise and green salad to serve (optional)

1 Put 4 eggs in cold water, bring to the boil, reduce heat and simmer for 3-4 minutes. Drain and transfer to a bowl of ice-cold water.
2 In a large bowl, mix together lamb, garlic, ginger, chilli, curry paste, peas and coriander; season. Divide into 4 equal portions.
3 Carefully peel boiled eggs and press an egg into the centre of each portion of lamb mixture, then gently wrap mixture around each egg until encased in mixture of 1cm (½in) even thickness. Preheat oven to 200°C/180°fan/Gas 6.
4 In a bowl, beat remaining egg. Put beaten egg, flour and breadcrumbs into separate small bowls. Dip each lamb portion into flour, then egg, then breadcrumbs to coat. Transfer to a lightly greased roasting tin and bake for 25 minutes. Serve with sweet chilli mayonnaise and a green salad, if you like.

Makes 4 • Time 50 mins
Calories 448 • Fibre 2.1g • Salt 0.9g • Sugar 0g
Fat 23g of which 8.6g is saturated

119

16 Monday

17 Tuesday

18 Wednesday

19 Thursday

20 Friday

REMINDERS

BLACKBERRY MINT MOJITO

Blackberries 24
Mint leaves 12, plus extra to serve
Limes 2
White rum 100ml (3½fl oz)
Ice cubes
Sugar 4 tsp
Soda water a dash

1 Put 20 blackberries, 160ml (5½fl oz) water, 12 mint leaves and juice of 1 lime in a cocktail shaker and mash with the end of a rolling pin (covered in clingfilm to prevent staining).
2 Add rum and some ice; shake well.
3 Put extra mint leaves and ice into two glasses and sieve in cocktail mixture. Stir 2 teaspoons sugar into each and add a dash of soda water. Cut remaining lime into wedges. Garnish drink with lime wedges, extra mint and remaining blackberries.

Serves 2 • **Time 5 mins**
Calories 161 • Fibre 2.5g • Salt 0g • Sugar 8g
Fat 0.2g of which 0g is saturated

23 Monday

24 Tuesday

25 Wednesday

26 Thursday

27 Friday

REMINDERS

Saturday 28

Sunday 29

HOMEMADE HERB CHEESE

Full-fat Greek yogurt 500g (1lb 2oz)
Salt 1 tsp
Chopped fresh parsley 3 tbsp
Chopped fresh chives 3 tbsp
Chopped fresh tarragon 3 tbsp
Toasted bread or vegetable batons
to serve (optional)

1 Line a large nylon sieve with clean muslin or a clean, fine tea towel and drape over a large bowl.
2 Mix yogurt and salt and pour through the sieve. Leave to drain for at least 12 hours, or overnight, in the fridge.
3 Gather up the muslin around the cheese and tie with string to make a ball. Suspend over the bowl in the fridge for a further 24 hours until the mixture has stopped dripping and has the texture of cream cheese.
4 Unwrap and divide into 8. Mix herbs and a little freshly ground black pepper together and roll each portion of cheese in the herb mixture. Put on a lined plate, cover and chill until ready to serve. Serve with toasted bread or vegetable batons, if you like.

TIP For a punchier cheese, mix 2 finely chopped spring onions with the herbs in place of the tarragon.

Serves 8 • Time 30 mins plus 2 days draining and chilling
Calories 83 • Fibre 0g • Salt 0g • Sugar 8g
Fat 6.4g of which 4.2g is saturated

123

30 Monday
(Last quarter
Bank Holiday, England, Wales, Northern Ireland

31 Tuesday

1 Wednesday SEPTEMBER

2 Thursday

3 Friday

REMINDERS

Saturday   4

Sunday   5

GALAXY STAR BUTTER BISCUITS

Butter 250g (9oz), softened
Icing sugar 350g (12oz)
Vanilla extract 1 tsp
Egg 1 large, yolk only
Plain flour 375g (13oz), sifted
Lemon 1, juice only
Food colouring paste 2 contrasting colours

1 Preheat oven to 190°C/170°fan/Gas 5 and line 2 baking trays with baking paper. Cream butter with 150g (5oz) icing sugar until light and fluffy.
2 Mix in vanilla extract and egg yolk, then fold in flour to form a firm dough. Wrap in clingfilm and chill for an hour.
3 On a floured surface, roll out chilled dough to a 3mm (⅛in) even thickness. Cut out stars using a star-shaped cutter. Re-roll trimmings until all dough has been used up.
4 Place on lined trays and bake for 10-12 minutes until golden-brown. Cool on wire racks.
5 In a wide, shallow bowl, mix remaining icing sugar with lemon juice and 3-4 tablespoons boiling water to make a glace icing.
6 Squeeze 3 small blobs of each food colour over icing, then swirl together with a skewer to create a marbled effect.
7 Dip cooled biscuits into icing, keeping as flat as possible, then place on wire racks to dry.

Makes 35–38 biscuits   •   Time 1 hr 10 mins plus chilling
Calories 132   •   Fibre 0.4g   •   Salt 0g   •   Sugar 10.4g
Fat 6.2g of which 3.8g is saturated

6 Monday

7 Tuesday
● New moon

8 Wednesday

9 Thursday

10 Friday

REMINDERS

Sunday 12

SPICED FRUIT

Plums 4, halved and stoned
Peaches or nectarines 2, halved and stoned
Ripe pears 2, peeled, halved and cored
Red wine 300ml (½ pint)
Light soft brown sugar 50g (2oz)
Fresh bay leaves 2
Vanilla pod 1, split
Cinnamon stick 1
Cream, ice cream, yogurt or a dairy-free alternative to serve

1 Preheat oven to 180°C/160°fan/Gas 4. Arrange all fruit cut-side up in a shallow baking dish. Pour over wine and sprinkle with sugar. Push bay, vanilla and cinnamon among fruit. Cover with foil and bake for 30 minutes.
2 Remove foil, baste with the wine and return to the oven for a further 45–60 minutes, basting occasionally, until fruit is tender.
3 Using a slotted spoon, remove the fruit and place in a heatproof dish; keep warm.
4 Strain cooking juices into a small saucepan and bring to the boil for about 5 minutes until reduced and syrupy. Pour mixture over fruit and leave to stand for 30 minutes before serving warm. Accompany with cream, ice cream, yogurt or a dairy-free alternative, if you prefer.

TIP Use unsweetened cranberry juice instead of red wine if preferred.

Serves 4 • Time 1¾ hours plus standing
Calories 163 • Fibre 3.6g • Salt 0g • Sugar 12.5g
Fat 0.2g of which 0g is saturated

127

13 Monday
⟩ First quarter

14 Tuesday

15 Wednesday

16 Thursday

17 Friday

REMINDERS

Saturday 18

Sunday 19

MINESTRONE SAUSAGE STEW WITH SALAMI CRISPS

Olive oil 2 tbsp
Thick pork sausages 6, each cut into 4 pieces
Onions 2, peeled and chopped
Garlic cloves 2, peeled and crushed
Celery stalks 2, trimmed and chopped
Carrots 2, peeled and chopped
Dried oregano 1½ tsp
Bay leaf 1
Chopped tomatoes 400g tin
Hot beef stock 600ml (1 pint)
White cabbage 225g (8oz), shredded
Cannellini beans 400g tin, drained and rinsed
Spaghetti 175g (6oz), broken into short lengths
Italian salami 8 slices
Crusty bread and basil leaves to serve
(optional)

1 Heat oil in a large pan, add sausages and cook, stirring, for 5 minutes until browned all over. Add onion, garlic, celery, carrots, oregano and bay, and cook for a further 5 minutes.
2 Stir in tomatoes and stock, bring to boil, add cabbage, cover and simmer for 15 minutes.
3 Stir in beans and spaghetti, bring back to boil, cover and simmer for 10 minutes until tender. Remove and discard bay leaf; season.
4 Meanwhile, dry fry salami for 3-4 minutes, turning, in a hot frying pan until crisp. Ladle stew into bowls and garnish with halved salami crisps. Serve with crusty bread and garnish with basil.

Serves 6 • Time 1 hr
Calories 576 • Fibre 21.3g • Salt 1.9g • Sugar 0g
Fat 22.6g of which 7.1g is saturated

20 Monday

○ Full moon

21 Tuesday

22 Wednesday

Autumnal equinox
Autumn begins

23 Thursday

24 Friday

REMINDERS

Saturday 25

Sunday 26

WIN

WIN A SOPHIE ALLPORT VOUCHER WORTH £150

Famous for their fine bone china and kitchen fabrics, Sophie Allport's designs celebrate all things British and are inspired by nature and the countryside.
You'll find a lovely range of bags and accessories, fragrance, products for children and pets and lots of gift ideas.
Shop online at sophieallport.com or phone 01778 560256.

Enter at **dairydiary.co.uk/win2021**
Or send in your name and address to:
Dairy Diary 2021 Prize Draw,
Eaglemoss, Electra House,
Electra Way, Crewe, CW1 6GL.
Closing date 30th November 2021

You can order your 2022 Dairy Diary via your milkman (see p170), or direct from the publisher at dairydiary.co.uk or by phoning 0344 4725265.

27 Monday

28 Tuesday

29 Wednesday
(Last quarter

30 Thursday

1 Friday OCTOBER

REMINDERS

Saturday 2

Sunday 3

TOFFEE APPLE CRUMBLE

Butter 150g (5oz), cut into small cubes
Rolled oats 150g (5oz)
Ground almonds 150g (5oz)
Demerara sugar 110g (4oz)
Cooking apples 2 large
Dessert apples 2 medium
Orange or lemon juice 1 tbsp
Golden syrup 3 tbsp
Fudge 50g (2oz), cut into thin slivers
Cream, **custard or ice cream** to serve
(optional)

1 Preheat oven to 200°C/180°fan/Gas 6. In
a bowl, rub butter, oats and almonds to an
even crumb. Add sugar and mix through.
2 Peel, quarter, core and thinly slice all
apples. Put in a 2 litre (3½ pint) ovenproof
dish. Sprinkle with juice, drizzle with syrup
and roughly mix in.
3 Spoon crumble mixture evenly over apples
and scatter with fudge slivers. Bake for 40
minutes until piping hot and lightly golden.
Stand for 10 minutes before serving with
cream, custard or ice cream, if you like.

TIPS Use light muscovado sugar for an even
richer taste. Opt for ready-chopped mini
fudge chunks if short on time.

Serves 8 • Time 1¼ hrs
Calories 440 • Fibre 1.8g • Salt 0.2g • Sugar 21g
Fat 28.3g of which 11.4g is saturated

133

4   Monday

5   Tuesday

6   Wednesday
● New moon

7   Thursday

8   Friday

REMINDERS

Sunday 10

CAULI MACARONI CHEESE

Small cauliflower florets 500g (1lb 2oz)
Vegetable oil 2 tbsp
Macaroni 200g (7oz)
Butter 75g (3oz)
Plain flour 75g (3oz)
Whole milk 900ml (1½ pints)
Wholegrain mustard 2 tbsp
Mature Cheddar 300g (11oz), grated
Dry white breadcrumbs 25g (1oz)
Salad to serve (optional)

1 Preheat oven to 200°C/180°fan/Gas 6 and line a baking tray with baking paper. Put florets in a bowl and toss in oil; season. Put on tray and bake for 30 minutes, turning occasionally, until lightly golden. Transfer to a 2 litre (3½ pint) ovenproof baking dish, cover and keep warm.
2 Meanwhile, cook macaroni according to packet's instructions. Drain, mix with florets, cover and keep warm.
3 Melt butter in a pan, stir in flour and cook gently, stirring, for 1 minute. Remove from heat and whisk in milk. Return to heat and boil, stirring, until thickened. Simmer for 1 minute.
4 Remove from heat, stir in mustard and 200g (7oz) cheese. Pour into cauliflower mixture; mix well. Top with remaining cheese and breadcrumbs.
5 Put dish on a baking tray and bake for 30 minutes until piping hot. Serve with salad, if liked.

Serves 4–6 • **Time 1¼ hrs**
Calories 634 • Fibre 4.1g • Salt 1.3g • Sugar 0g
Fat 38.5g of which 21.3g is saturated

135

11 Monday

12 Tuesday

13 Wednesday
) First quarter

14 Thursday

15 Friday

REMINDERS

Sunday 17

ROAST BEETROOT & GINGER SOUP

Beetroot 4, scrubbed, topped and tailed, and cut into thick wedges
Red onions 2, peeled and cut into thick wedges
Root ginger 25g (1oz), peeled and cut into thick slices
Celery 2 sticks, cut into thick chunks
Olive oil 2 tbsp
Vegetable stock pots or stock cubes 2
Celery salt 1-2 tsp
Lime or lemon juice 1-2 tbsp
Coconut milk yogurt 125g pot
Torn celery leaves to garnish (optional)

1 Preheat oven to 160°C/140°fan/Gas 3. Put beetroot, onions, ginger and celery in a roasting tin. Add oil and mix well to coat. Cover with foil and roast for 3 hours until vegetables have softened.
2 Put half the roasted vegetables in a food processor with one of the stock pots or cubes and 500ml (18fl oz) boiling water. Whizz until smooth, then tip into a large saucepan. Repeat process with remaining roasted vegetables, cooking juices from tin, remaining stock pot and 500ml (18fl oz) boiling water.
3 Stir in celery salt, pepper and juice to taste. If necessary, reheat gently and adjust consistency and seasoning to taste. Ladle into warmed bowls, then swirl yogurt into each and sprinkle with celery leaves, if using.

Serves 6–8 • Time 3¼ hrs
Calories 90 • Fibre 2.8g • Salt 2g • Sugar 0g
Fat 4.9g of which 0.9g is saturated

137

18 Monday

Don't forget to order your **2022 Dairy Diary**. Use the order form on page 170 or order online.
If you don't have a milkman, call 0344 4725265 or visit www.dairydiary.co.uk

19 Tuesday

20 Wednesday

○ Full moon

21 Thursday

22 Friday

REMINDERS

Saturday 23

Sunday 24

BLACK PUDDING POTATOES

Goose or duck fat 2 tbsp
Garlic 1 clove, peeled and quartered
Thyme 4 sprigs
Potatoes 4 large, scrubbed and thinly sliced
Black pudding 110g (4oz)
Hot chicken stock 400ml (14fl oz)

1 Preheat oven to 170°C/150°fan/Gas 3. In a small pan, warm fat with garlic and thyme until sizzling, then leave to infuse. Layer half the potato slices in a 1.5 litre (2½ pint) ovenproof dish, spooning over a little fat and seasoning as you go.
2 Crumble black pudding over, then layer over remaining potatoes. Pour over hot stock, then spoon over remaining fat and season. Cover with foil and put dish on a baking sheet.
3 Bake for 1½ hours, then remove foil and increase oven temperature to 220°C/200°fan/Gas 7. Bake for 20–30 minutes until crisp and golden.

TIP Enjoy with roast chicken or pork.

Serves 6 • Time 2 hrs 20 mins
Calories 189 • Fibre 2.7g • Salt 0.8g • Sugar 0g
Fat 9g of which 3.6g is saturated

25 Monday

26 Tuesday

27 Wednesday

28 Thursday
(Last quarter

29 Friday

REMINDERS

Saturday 30
Don't forget to put your clocks back **1** hour tonight
(t.b.c. dependent on Government ruling)

Sunday 31
Halloween

TARANTULA TRUFFLES

Dark chocolate 75g, broken into pieces
Mini chocolate brownie bites 200g (7oz), crumbled
Seedless raspberry jam 100g (3½oz)
Chocolate orange sticks 32
Edible eye cake decorations 16
Chocolate vermicelli 25g

1 Put dark chocolate in a heatproof bowl set over a pan of barely simmering water until melted. Remove bowl from heat and leave to cool for 10 minutes.
2 Stir in brownie crumbs and 75g (3oz) jam. Cover and chill for 30 minutes until firm enough to shape.
3 Divide mixture into 8 equal portions. One at a time, break off a small piece for the head and a small piece for the body and form each into balls. Gently press the head onto the body, flattening edges slightly, then place on a board lined with baking paper. Repeat until mixture has been used up.
4 Break chocolate sticks in half and poke into the sides of the spiders to resemble legs. Chill for 1 hour until firm.
5 Carefully brush the backs of the eyes with jam and stick in place on each spider. Brush the bodies lightly with more jam, if needed, and sprinkle with chocolate vermicelli for a hairy appearance. If warm, chill for 30 minutes to firm up before serving.

Makes 8 • **Time 45 mins plus chilling**
Calories 327 • Fibre 1.6g • Salt 0.2g • Sugar 33.9g
Fat 16.7g of which 9.5g is saturated

141

1 Monday

2 Tuesday

3 Wednesday

4 Thursday
● New moon

5 Friday
Bonfire Night

REMINDERS

GAMMON & APPLE COBBLER

Butter 75g (3oz)
Onion 1, peeled and chopped
Eating apples 2, peeled, cored and thickly sliced
Lean unsmoked gammon 500g (1lb 2oz), cut into 2cm (¾in) pieces
Hot chicken stock 200ml (7fl oz)
Dry cider or fresh apple juice 150ml (¼ pint)
Dried sage 1 tsp
Cornflour 2 tbsp
Double cream 6 tbsp
Self-raising flour 250g (9oz)
Mature Cheddar 100g (3½oz), grated

1 Melt 25g (1oz) butter in a pan and fry onion and apples for 5 minutes. Add gammon and continue to cook, stirring, for a further 5 minutes.
2 Pour over stock and cider or juice, add sage, bring to the boil and simmer for 10 minutes.
3 Mix cornflour and half the cream to a paste, then stir into gammon mixture. Cook, stirring, for 2 minutes until thickened; season. Put in a 1.5 litre (2½ pint) gratin dish; cover with foil.
4 Preheat oven to 200°C/180°fan/Gas 6. Sift flour into a bowl, rub in remaining butter and stir in most of cheese. Mix 2 tbsp cream with 7 tbsp water, then mix into flour mixture. Turn dough out onto a floured surface and knead until smooth. Roll out to 1cm (½in) thickness and cut out 12 rounds with a 5cm (2in) round cutter.
5 Remove foil from gammon. Arrange rounds around edge of dish, glaze with remaining cream,

Serves 4 • Time 1 hr 10 mins
Calories 861 • Fibre 3.8g • Salt 4g • Sugar 0g
Fat 51g of which 28.7g is saturated

sprinkle with remaining cheese and stand on a baking tray. Bake for 25-30 minutes until piping hot, golden and bubbling.

8   Monday

9   Tuesday

10 Wednesday

11 Thursday
) First quarter

12 Friday

REMINDERS

CURRIED PARSNIP BHAJIS

Fresh coriander 25g (1oz), chopped
Mango 1 small, peeled, stoned and chopped
Cucumber 75g, finely chopped
Cherry tomatoes 6, quartered
White balsamic vinegar 4 tsp
Gram flour 250g (9oz)
Medium curry powder 1 tbsp
Salt 1 tsp
Onion 1 medium, peeled and finely sliced
Parsnip 175g (6oz), peeled and grated
Sunflower oil 2 litres (3½ pints), for
deep frying

1 Mix 2 tbsp coriander with mango,
cucumber, tomatoes and vinegar to make a
relish; season to taste. Cover and chill.
2 Sift flour into a bowl and stir in curry
powder and 1 tsp salt. Mix in onion, parsnip
and remaining coriander until well coated,
then gradually blend in 150ml (5fl oz) cold
water to make a thick batter.
3 In a deep frying pan, heat oil to 180°C
(350°F). Using a dessert spoon, drop
flattened spoonfuls of batter into the oil,
working in batches of 6 or 7 at a time. Fry
for 7-8 minutes, turning in the oil, until crisp
and golden.
4 Drain on kitchen paper and keep warm
while frying remaining mixture. Serve warm
with mango relish.

TIP Use ordinary balsamic vinegar, if preferred.

Makes 20 • **Time 45 mins**
Calories 78 • Fibre 2.2g • Salt 0.3g • Sugar 0g
Fat 3.1g of which 0.4g is saturated

15 Monday

16 Tuesday

17 Wednesday

18 Thursday

19 Friday
○ Full moon

REMINDERS

BROWN SUGAR MERINGUES

Eggs 2, whites only
Light muscovado sugar 65g (2½oz)
Caster sugar 50g (2oz)
Double cream 150ml (¼ pint)
Ground cinnamon ¼ tsp
Dark chocolate 50g (2oz), chopped (optional)

1 Preheat oven to 110°C/90°fan/Gas ¼. Line a large baking sheet with a sheet of non-stick baking paper. In a large bowl, whisk egg whites with an electric whisk until stiff and the bowl can be turned upside down without the meringue moving.
2 In a separate bowl, mix 50g (2oz) muscovado sugar with all caster sugar, then gradually whisk into egg whites a teaspoon at a time. Continue to whisk for 1-2 minutes until mixture is very thick and glossy.
3 Scoop up a heaped dessert spoon of meringue mixture. Using a second dessert spoon, ease mixture onto lined sheet in a neat oval shape. Continue until all of mixture has been shaped to make about 20 meringues.
4 Bake for 1-1¼ hours until they can be lifted off the paper easily. Leave to cool completely.
5 Just before serving, pour cream into a bowl, add the remaining muscovado sugar and cinnamon and whisk to soft swirls, then use to sandwich the meringues together. Arrange in paper cases.
6 If using, place chocolate in a heatproof bowl set over a pan of just simmering water and stir until melted. Drizzle over meringues to serve.

Makes 10 pairs • Time 1½ hrs
Calories 147 • Fibre 0.2g • Salt 0g • Sugar 15g
Fat 9.5g of which 5.8g is saturated

22 Monday

23 Tuesday

24 Wednesday

25 Thursday

26 Friday

REMINDERS

Saturday 27
(Last quarter

Sunday 28
First Sunday in Advent

PHEASANT WITH PEARS & BLACK PUDDING

Butter 125g (4½ oz)
Onion 1 small, peeled and finely chopped
Black pudding 175g (6oz), crumbled
Fresh white breadcrumbs 175g (6oz)
Dried sage 1 tsp
Egg 1 medium, beaten
Oven-ready pheasants 2 x 650g (1lb 6oz)
Smoked streaky bacon 6 rashers, halved
Firm pears 4, peeled, cored and halved
Lemon 1 small, juice only
Clear honey 1 tbsp
Fresh watercress to garnish

1 Preheat oven to 220°C/200°fan/Gas 7. In a pan, melt 50g (2oz) butter and fry onion for 5 minutes until softened. Cool for 10 minutes.
2 In a bowl, mix black pudding, breadcrumbs, sage, egg, onions and seasoning. Shape into 12 balls. Chill, covered.
3 Smear pheasants with 40g (1½oz) butter; season. Lay bacon over birds in a criss-cross pattern and put in a roasting tin. Bake for 20 minutes, then reduce to 180°C/160°fan/Gas 4 and cook for 35-40 minutes more, basting occasionally, until cooked through. Add stuffing balls for last 30 minutes, basting in the juices.
4 Meanwhile, put pears in a baking dish and dot with remaining butter. Mix lemon juice and honey; pour over pears. Bake for 30 minutes until tender. Rest for 15 minutes before serving.
5 Drain pheasants and place on a platter with pears and stuffing balls. Garnish with watercress.

Serves 4 • Time 1 hr 30 mins
Calories 797 • Fibre 3.1g • Salt 2.4g • Sugar 3.8g
Fat 45.1g of which 19.8g is saturated

149

29 Monday

30 Tuesday
St Andrew's Day

1 Wednesday DECEMBER

2 Thursday

3 Friday

REMINDERS

DECEMBER

Saturday 4
● New moon

Sunday 5

NUTTY FRUIT CAKES

Golden syrup 150g (5oz)
Butter 75g (3oz)
Light brown sugar 75g (3oz)
Whole milk 150ml (5fl oz)
Self-raising flour 200g (7oz)
Ground mixed spice 1 tsp
Pecans 50g (2oz), chopped
Mixed dried fruit 175g (6oz)
Icing sugar 175g (6oz)
Cocoa powder 2 tbsp
Whisky 2 tbsp
Pecan halves 12

1 Preheat oven to 180°C/160°fan/Gas 4. Grease a 12-hole muffin tin. Put syrup, butter and brown sugar in a pan and heat gently until melted. Remove from the heat and stir in milk.
2 Add flour, spice, chopped pecans and fruit and mix well to a thick batter. Divide equally between the prepared tins, smooth the tops and bake for 30 minutes until risen, firm to the touch and lightly golden. Cool for 15 minutes before turning onto a wire rack to cool completely.
3 Sift icing sugar and cocoa into a bowl. Gradually mix in whisky and 2-3 tsp water to make a smooth, spreadable icing.
4 Spread icing thickly on top of each cooled cake, allowing it to drip down the sides. Top each with a pecan half and leave to stand for a few minutes until icing is set.

Makes 12 • Time 50 mins plus cooling and setting
Calories 328 • Fibre 1.7g • Salt 0.3g • Sugar 31.3g
Fat 11.1g of which 4.1g is saturated

151

6 Monday

7 Tuesday

8 Wednesday

9 Thursday

10 Friday

REMINDERS

Saturday 11
> First quarter

Sunday 12

CHOCOLATE ORANGE PANETTONE BUNS

Milk 2 tbsp
Fast action dried yeast 7g sachet
Caster sugar 50g (2oz)
Unsalted butter 125g (4½oz), softened
Eggs 2 medium
Strong white bread flour 250g (9oz)
Dark chocolate 75g (3oz), chopped
Mixed dried fruit with candied peel 75g (3oz)
Orange extract 1 tsp

1 Place milk in a small bowl and warm in microwave for 15 seconds. Mix in yeast and 1 teaspoon sugar.
2 Put remaining sugar in a bowl with butter and cream together until pale and fluffy. Beat in eggs, one at a time, adding a little flour to prevent splitting if needed.
3 Add yeast mixture, a pinch salt and flour and mix with a knife for 10 minutes. Cover with oiled clingfilm and leave in a warm place for 2 hours or until doubled in size.
4 Add chocolate, fruit and orange extract and knead for 5 minutes.
5 Divide into 6 and place in a greased deep six-hole muffin tin. Re-cover with clingfilm and leave in a warm place for 1 hour.
6 Preheat oven to 180°C/160°fan/Gas 4. Bake for 20 minutes until risen and golden-brown. Cool on a wire rack.

Serves 6 • Time 1 hr plus proving
Calories 459 • Fibre 2.2g • Salt 0.1g • Sugar 19.4g
Fat 22.8g of which 13.6g is saturated

153

13 Monday

14 Tuesday

15 Wednesday

16 Thursday

17 Friday

REMINDERS

Saturday 18

Sunday 19
○ Full moon

BALSAMIC & HONEY ROASTED SPROUTS

Brussels sprouts 450g (1lb), trimmed
Eating apples 2, cored and cut into thick wedges
Red onion 1, peeled and thickly sliced
Pancetta or thick smoked bacon 110g (4oz), thickly sliced
Fresh sage leaves 8
Olive oil 1 tbsp
Balsamic vinegar 2 tbsp
Runny honey 1 tbsp
Roast meat and vegetables to serve (optional)

1 Preheat oven to 200°C/180°fan/Gas 6. Line a large baking tray with baking paper. Bring a pan of salted water to the boil, add sprouts and cook for 1 minute. Drain and rinse under cold running water to cool. Drain again. Place in a large bowl.

2 Mix in apples, onion, pancetta or bacon and sage. Shake oil, vinegar and honey in a jar to combine, then pour over the bowl and toss to combine.

3 Spread mixture over the lined tray, season and cover with foil. Bake for 20 minutes, then remove the foil and cook for a further 20 minutes until tender. Discard sage and serve immediately to accompany roast meats and other vegetables, if you like.

Serves 4 • **Time 50 mins**
Calories 163 • Fibre 7g • Salt 0.8g • Sugar 4g
Fat 7.6g of which 2.5g is saturated

155

20 Monday

. . . .

21 Tuesday
Winter solstice
Winter begins

. . . .

22 Wednesday

. . . .

23 Thursday

. . . .

24 Friday
Christmas Eve

. . . .

REMINDERS

Saturday 25
Christmas Day

Sunday 26
Boxing Day

MINCE PIE LINZER TORTE

Plain flour 150g (5oz)
Ground cinnamon ½ tsp
Unsalted butter 75g (3oz)
Ground almonds 50g (2oz)
Caster sugar 50g (2oz)
Lemon 1 small, finely grated zest and juice
Eggs 3 medium, yolks only
Vegetarian mincemeat 300g (11oz)
Eating apple 1, cored and grated
Whole milk 1 tbsp
Whipped cream to serve (optional)

1 Sift flour and cinnamon into a bowl and rub in butter until mixture resembles breadcrumbs. Stir in almonds, sugar and zest. Mix in 2 yolks and enough lemon juice and water to make a firm dough. Wrap in clingfilm and chill for 30 minutes.
2 Grease a 20 x 4cm (8 x 1½in) loose-bottomed flan tin. Knead dough to soften. Slice off 75g (3oz) for decoration, then roll out remaining dough on a floured surface to fit tin. Neaten edges.
3 Mix mincemeat and apple; spread over base of pastry. Roll out reserved pastry on a floured surface to a rectangle measuring 18 x 10cm (7 x 5in); cut into 10 strips and lay across filling in a lattice. Tuck ends between filling and case; chill for 30 minutes.
4 Preheat oven to 190°C/170°fan/Gas 5. Mix remaining yolk with milk and brush over lattice and edges. Put on a baking tray and bake for 40 minutes until crisp. Cool for 20 minutes in tin before easing out. Serve warm or cold with whipped cream, if you like.

Serves 8 • **1 hr plus chilling and cooling**
Calories 332 • Fibre 1.6g • Salt 0.1g • Sugar 20.4g
Fat 14.9g of which 5.8g is saturated

157

27 Monday
(Last quarter
Bank Holiday, UK

28 Tuesday
Bank Holiday, UK

29 Wednesday

30 Thursday

31 Friday
New Year's Eve

REMINDERS

TAHINI TURKEY WITH PERSIAN RICE

Basmati rice 225g (8oz), rinsed
Rapeseed oil 3 tbsp
Onions 2, peeled and thinly sliced
Cooked turkey 350-400g (12-14oz), shredded
Garlic 2 cloves, peeled and crushed (optional)
Greek-style yogurt 150g pot
Tahini paste 2 tbsp
Pistachios 25g (1oz), roughly chopped
Pomegranate seeds 125g (4½oz)
Chopped fresh mint 15g (½oz)
Lemon wedges to serve (optional)

1 Add rice to a large pan of salted boiling water. Simmer for 8 minutes, then drain, rinse with cold water and set aside.
2 Place pan over a medium heat, add 2 tablespoons of oil and onions; season. Cook, stirring occasionally, for 8 minutes until softened and golden. Stir in rice, cover tightly and cook over a low heat for 8-10 minutes.
3 Heat remaining oil in a wok or large frying pan until hot, add turkey and garlic, if using, and fry until crispy. Meanwhile, mix yogurt and tahini in a bowl; season.
4 Stir pistachios, pomegranate seeds and mint into rice. Spoon onto plates. Arrange turkey on top with tahini yogurt. Serve with lemon wedges, if you like.

Serves 4 • Time 35 mins
Calories 644 • Fibre 5.7g • Salt 0.3g • Sugar 0g
Fat 28.9g of which 5.8g is saturated

159

3 Monday
Bank Holiday, UK

4 Tuesday
Bank Holiday, Scotland

5 Wednesday

6 Thursday

7 Friday

REMINDERS

NOTES

NOTES

NOTES

NOTES

Three ways to order your Dairy Diary

FROM YOUR MILKMAN
Use the **order form overleaf**, or, if you usually order via your dairy's website, please order online.

TELEPHONE
If you do not have a milkman, call **0344 4725265.**
Your diary will be posted to you.

ONLINE
Visit **dairydiary.co.uk**
See full details of the 2022 Dairy Diary and other great products.

DISCOVER MORE RECIPES & FABULOUS COMPETITIONS
Visit **dairydiary.co.uk**
Follow us on **Twitter** @thedairydiary
Follow us on **Facebook** dairydiary

Reserve your Dairy Diary 2022

To reserve your copy of the 2022 Dairy Diary, please fill in the form overleaf and leave it out with your empties from September onwards.

If you usually order via your dairy's website, please order online.

Order form overleaf...

Dairy Diary

2022

Order form

MILKMAN PLEASE LEAVE ME

[ ] copies of the **Dairy Diary 2022**

[ ] copies of the **Dairy Diary Set**

Name _____

Address _____

_____

_____

_____

Postcode _____

THANK YOU

Please leave out for your milkman from September 2021 onwards

THERE ARE LOTS MORE RECIPES AT
DAIRYDIARY.CO.UK

RECIPE NOTES

- Nutritional information has been calculated by portion or item. Where there are portion variations, e.g. serves 6-8, the analysis given is based on the larger number.
- Spoon measures are level unless otherwise stated.
- Eggs are large unless otherwise stated.
- Sugar is 'free sugars' (added sugars, including those naturally present in fruit juice, honey & syrups, but excluding the natural sugars present in all fruit and vegetables).
- Recipes that do not contain animal products (such as meat, fish, poultry, dairy, eggs and honey) are suitable for vegans. Please check ingredients carefully for dietary suitability.

SAFETY NOTES

- Recipes using nuts or nut products are not suitable for young children or those with a nut allergy.
- Certain at-risk groups, such as pregnant women, babies and sick or elderly people should not eat raw or lightly cooked eggs.

V Suitable for vegetarians, provided a suitable cheese, yogurt or pesto etc. is used.

F Suitable for freezing.

PLANNER 2022

JANUARY	FEBRUARY	MARCH
1 Sat	1 Tue	1 Tue
2 Sun	2 Wed	2 Wed
3 Mon BANK HOLIDAY UK	3 Thu	3 Thu
4 Tue BANK HOLIDAY SCOTLAND	4 Fri	4 Fri
5 Wed	5 Sat	5 Sat
6 Thu	6 Sun	6 Sun
7 Fri	7 Mon	7 Mon
8 Sat	8 Tue	8 Tue
9 Sun	9 Wed	9 Wed
10 Mon	10 Thu	10 Thu
11 Tue	11 Fri	11 Fri
12 Wed	12 Sat	12 Sat
13 Thu	13 Sun	13 Sun
14 Fri	14 Mon	14 Mon
15 Sat	15 Tue	15 Tue
16 Sun	16 Wed	16 Wed
17 Mon	17 Thu	17 Thu BANK HOLIDAY N. IRELAND
18 Tue	18 Fri	18 Fri
19 Wed	19 Sat	19 Sat
20 Thu	20 Sun	20 Sun
21 Fri	21 Mon	21 Mon
22 Sat	22 Tue	22 Tue
23 Sun	23 Wed	23 Wed
24 Mon	24 Thu	24 Thu
25 Tue	25 Fri	25 Fri
26 Wed	26 Sat	26 Sat
27 Thu	27 Sun	27 Sun
28 Fri	28 Mon	28 Mon
29 Sat		29 Tue
30 Sun		30 Wed
31 Mon		31 Thu

APRIL		MAY		JUNE	
1	Fri	1	Sun	1	Wed
2	Sat	2	Mon BANK HOLIDAY UK	2	Thu
3	Sun	3	Tue	3	Fri
4	Mon	4	Wed	4	Sat
5	Tue	5	Thu	5	Sun
6	Wed	6	Fri	6	Mon
7	Thu	7	Sat	7	Tue
8	Fri	8	Sun	8	Wed
9	Sat	9	Mon	9	Thu
10	Sun	10	Tue	10	Fri
11	Mon	11	Wed	11	Sat
12	Tue	12	Thu	12	Sun
13	Wed	13	Fri	13	Mon
14	Thu	14	Sat	14	Tue
15	Fri BANK HOLIDAY UK	15	Sun	15	Wed
16	Sat	16	Mon	16	Thu
17	Sun	17	Tue	17	Fri
18	Mon BANK HOLIDAY UK (EXCL. SCOTLAND)	18	Wed	18	Sat
19	Tue	19	Thu	19	Sun
20	Wed	20	Fri	20	Mon
21	Thu	21	Sat	21	Tue
22	Fri	22	Sun	22	Wed
23	Sat	23	Mon	23	Thu
24	Sun	24	Tue	24	Fri
25	Mon	25	Wed	25	Sat
26	Tue	26	Thu	26	Sun
27	Wed	27	Fri	27	Mon
28	Thu	28	Sat	28	Tue
29	Fri	29	Sun	29	Wed
30	Sat	30	Mon BANK HOLIDAY UK	30	Thu
		31	Tue		

P.T.O. July–December 2022

PLANNER 2022

JULY		AUGUST		SEPTEMBER	
1	Fri	1	Mon BANK HOLIDAY SCOTLAND	1	Thu
2	Sat	2	Tue	2	Fri
3	Sun	3	Wed	3	Sat
4	Mon	4	Thu	4	Sun
5	Tue	5	Fri	5	Mon
6	Wed	6	Sat	6	Tue
7	Thu	7	Sun	7	Wed
8	Fri	8	Mon	8	Thu
9	Sat	9	Tue	9	Fri
10	Sun	10	Wed	10	Sat
11	Mon	11	Thu	11	Sun
12	Tue BANK HOLIDAY N. IRELAND	12	Fri	12	Mon
13	Wed	13	Sat	13	Tue
14	Thu	14	Sun	14	Wed
15	Fri	15	Mon	15	Thu
16	Sat	16	Tue	16	Fri
17	Sun	17	Wed	17	Sat
18	Mon	18	Thu	18	Sun
19	Tue	19	Fri	19	Mon
20	Wed	20	Sat	20	Tue
21	Thu	21	Sun	21	Wed
22	Fri	22	Mon	22	Thu
23	Sat	23	Tue	23	Fri
24	Sun	24	Wed	24	Sat
25	Mon	25	Thu	25	Sun
26	Tue	26	Fri	26	Mon
27	Wed	27	Sat	27	Tue
28	Thu	28	Sun	28	Wed
29	Fri	29	Mon BANK HOLIDAY UK (EXCL. SCOTLAND)	29	Thu
30	Sat	30	Tue	30	Fri
31	Sun	31	Wed		

OCTOBER	NOVEMBER	DECEMBER
1 Sat	1 Tue	1 Thu
2 Sun	2 Wed	2 Fri
3 Mon	3 Thu	3 Sat
4 Tue	4 Fri	4 Sun
5 Wed	5 Sat	5 Mon
6 Thu	6 Sun	6 Tue
7 Fri	7 Mon	7 Wed
8 Sat	8 Tue	8 Thu
9 Sun	9 Wed	9 Fri
10 Mon	10 Thu	10 Sat
11 Tue	11 Fri	11 Sun
12 Wed	12 Sat	12 Mon
13 Thu	13 Sun	13 Tue
14 Fri	14 Mon	14 Wed
15 Sat	15 Tue	15 Thu
16 Sun	16 Wed	16 Fri
17 Mon	17 Thu	17 Sat
18 Tue	18 Fri	18 Sun
19 Wed	19 Sat	19 Mon
20 Thu	20 Sun	20 Tue
21 Fri	21 Mon	21 Wed
22 Sat	22 Tue	22 Thu
23 Sun	23 Wed	23 Fri
24 Mon	24 Thu	24 Sat
25 Tue	25 Fri	25 Sun
26 Wed	26 Sat	26 Mon BANK HOLIDAY UK
27 Thu	27 Sun	27 Tue BANK HOLIDAY UK
28 Fri	28 Mon	28 Wed
29 Sat	29 Tue	29 Thu
30 Sun	30 Wed	30 Fri
31 Mon		31 Sat

ACKNOWLEDGEMENTS

Executive Editor
Emily Davenport

Author/Editor
Louise Burfitt

Art Editor
Graham Meigh

Recipe Editor
Maggie Ramsay

Production
Sema Sant Anna

Recipes
Sharon Axson
Emily Davenport
Kathryn Hawkins
Kate Moseley

Photographer
Steve Lee

Food Stylist
Sara Lewis

Props Stylist
India Jackson

Recipe testing
Emily Bagshaw
Lucy Goodman
Katy Hackforth
Hannah Nadin
Jake Wilshaw

Nutritional analysis
Paul McArdle

Special thanks
BerryWorld
Aune Butt
Heather Munro
Emma Snow
Denise Spencer-Walker

Published by Eaglemoss Ltd

Barn 3, Somerford Business Court, Somerford, Congleton, CW12 4SN

Dairy Diary orders telephone: 0344 4725265

Queries telephone: 01270 270050

Website: dairydiary.co.uk

Email: enquiries@dairydiary.co.uk

While every care has been taken in compiling the information in this Diary, the publishers cannot accept responsibility for any errors, inadvertent or not, that may be found or may occur at some time in future owing to changes in legislation or any other reason. © Eaglemoss Ltd 2019/2020

ISBN 978-1-911388-33-3

PICTURE CREDITS

Cover Shutterstock/artjazz; 21 Shutterstock/Hannamariah; 22 Shutterstock/Dan Breckwoldt; 23 Pictorial Press Ltd/Alamy Stock Photo; 29 Shutterstock/Daniel_Kay; 26 Pixabay/PublicDomainPictures; 27 Shutterstock/fizkes; 28 Shutterstock/Pedro Turrini Neto; 29 Shutterstock/Aquarius Studio; 30 Pixabay/jekar1588; 31 Pixabay/sohnji10131; 32 The National Piping Centre Museum; 33 Shutterstock/Yuthana Choradet Ness; 34 & 7 Old Operating Theatre Museum & Herb Garret; 35 i4images rm/Alamy Stock Photo; 36 Pixabay/Oldiefan; 37 Pixabay/PeterDargatz; 37 Pixabay/andyballard; 38 Shutterstock/Sean Xu; 39 Shutterstock/MarjanCermelj; 40 Shutterstock/Coatesy; 41 Pixabay/SimKlipp99; 42 Pixabay/RitaE; 43 Adobe Stock/avoferten; 44 Adobe Stock/sewcream; 45 Shutterstock/Melica; 45 Eaglemoss/Steve Lee; 46 Shutterstock/fotohunter; 50 Shutterstock/FamVeld; 53–159 Eaglemoss/Steve Lee except 103; 117; 121 berryworld.com and 77; 83; 119 simplybeefandlamb.co.uk